The

Throu

partic...arly true ...st be returned on or before the date last stamped ...ent for infertility. Of greatest concern has been ... er order births: in the UK alone, numbers of triplets have trebled in the las...

Families with multiple births face very specific problems and there is now a growing awareness that many professionals have insufficient experience to provide optimum care, support and advice.

Over the past twenty years, parent-led organisations have successfully provided a large measure of mutual support but health care professionals have been slow to follow their lead. The Multiple Births Foundation (MBF) was therefore founded in 1988 by consultant paediatrician, Dr Elizabeth Bryan, MD FRCP FRCPCH, with dual aims: primarily, to inform professionals about the special requirements of multiple birth families through a comprehensive education programme and, secondly, to provide some direct services to the families, including specialist clinics and telephone consultations. The MBF has also published a wide range of written information for parents and professionals.

The MBF was funded by, among others, the European Union to produce the first written guidelines for the care of families with multiple births. These are aimed at the wide spectrum of professionals involved - including infertility specialists, those concerned with obstetric and paediatric care (both in hospital and the community), teachers and social workers. The First Five Years and Beyond is the latest addition to the series.

In the first instance, the Guidelines relate to the health care structure in the United Kingdom, with a view to the eventual translation and adaptation of the text for individual countries.

How to use them

The aim of the Guidelines is to produce easily accessible information quickly. The recommendations are not intended as a rigid set of rules but rather as a framework upon which the professional can base a care plan that will meet individual requirements at each stage.

To simplify its use, the text has been divided into sections covering different aspects of care. Areas which may need special consideration are described in the **Background**, with specific **Recommendations** on how best to respond listed on the page opposite.

In order to ensure ...ay be reiterated.
Cross reference to ...ere appropriate.
Scientific reference ...nt UK support
organisations can b

A superscript M in ...ler further
reading) is availabl

We have referred ...a clear distinction from the mother.

Contents

Contents

FF4

General Introduction

To be the mother of twins is the dream of many women but the reality may not live up to expectations. The challenge of looking after and responding to two babies, each of whom is likely to be more vulnerable than the average singleton, can be very daunting. This can be compounded by the common perception that twins bring unqualified joy from conception onwards. Such a reaction can make it very hard for families to admit their difficulties and to get the professional help they need. Physical, emotional and financial strains in the early days may lead to relationship difficulties. Indeed, divorce amongst parents of twins has been found to be more common in those who had had poor support during the first year[1].

Multiple birth children tend to be at a disadvantage from the start. The mean gestation and birthweight for twins are significantly less than that of single born infants: 37 weeks compared with 40 weeks and 2500g compared with 3500g[2]. Due to these factors, twins are more likely to suffer from neonatal complications (see **Multiple Pregnancy**). These can lead to long-term morbidity such as cerebral palsy and learning difficulties (see **Special Needs in Twins and More**).

The upbringing of two or more children of the same age is inevitably different to that of singleton children. Different environmental factors will be discussed in more detail later but they include the shared mother infant relationship, triadic communication, lack of solitude, reduced opportunity and the intrapair relationship.

Problems (some of them requiring expensive remedial intervention) may occur later on if the children are not treated as individuals from the start and if the families are not given appropriate guidance and support from pregnancy onwards.

Background

Zygosity Determination[M]

There are two types of twins: monozygotic (MZ or 'identical') and dizygotic (DZ, 'fraternal' or 'non-identical'). Triplets may be trizygotic (TZ), DZ or MZ. Even quins who are MZ have been reported[3]. There are medical reasons why zygosity should be determined as soon as possible. It is also of fundamental importance to many parents of twins and higher order births (and later to the children themselves) to know as soon as possible whether they are MZ or DZ. Furthermore, accurate zygosity determination is essential for any twins who participate in the large number of twin studies (see **Facts about Multiple Births**).

Reasons

Medical and developmental

- to judge the significance of discordant growth rates or psychomotor development in the children
- to determine the risk of inheritance in some forms of genetic disease
- to gauge the potential for organ transplantation

Parental

- to assess the chances of having subsequent multiple births
- to understand the significance of similar or dissimilar growth and development in their twins
- to satisfy their natural interest in the children
- to reinforce their resolve to treat their children as separate individuals if they are MZ
- to enable them to answer the most frequently asked question 'Are they identical?'

Scientific research

- to determine the relative contributions of genetics and environment to human development, behaviour and disease

continued over

Zygosity Determination^M

■ Zygosity determination should be routinely available for all multiple birth infants and children

■ Professional carers should be reminded of:

 the difference between zygosity and chorionicity

 the importance of zygosity determination

 the implications of both

continued over

Background

Zygosity Determination continued

Methods

Sex

One third of all UK twins are boy/girl pairs and they must be dizygotic (except for rare instances of MZ twins where one has an XO chromosome anomaly).

Chorionicity[4]

If the placenta has a single chorion (outer sac) then the twins must be MZ. However, one third of MZ twins have two chorions, as do all DZ twins. Thus <u>no</u> indication of zygosity can be derived from the placenta in about half of Caucasian* twins, that is those of like sex with dichorionic placentae. Many clinicians are still ignorant of this fact. Chorionicity can of course only be established during pregnancy (by ultrasound assessment) or at birth.

Blood genetic markers

Analysis of a large number of biochemical genetic markers such as blood groups can provide a probability of over 95% that the twins are MZ. If one marker is different, the twins are DZ (although this should always be verified by repeat testing to allow for laboratory error).

DNA

DNA 'fingerprint' patterns from blood and other tissues are the most reliable methods of zygosity determination. A cheek swab is the least invasive and most accessible means of collecting DNA from newborn infants as well as from older children.

Physical Features

Although a commonly used method in the past, physical appearance cannot be used as an accurate method of determining zygosity. At birth MZ twins can look very different. Although by two years the following features are useful indicators, they are not infallible: colour and texture of hair, colour of eyes, shape of ears, teeth eruption pattern and formation, shape of hands and feet, and pattern of growth. Some DZ twins can look very alike and occasionally MZ twins may have distinctly different physical features, even hair colour[5].

*The proportion varies in different racial groups

continued over

Zygosity Determination continued

Methods

■ Determine zygosity by the following stages (see flow chart in **Facts about Multiple Births**):

  Sex: boy/girl twins must be dizygotic

  Chorionicity (if a reliable report on placental examination is available): monochorionic pairs must be MZ. (NB like sex dichorionic pairs can be MZ)

  Analysis of DNA: because of the accuracy and the ease of sample collection[†], this method is to be preferred to multiple genetic marker testing

  Physical features: these should only be used when other methods are not available

[†]Details of how to obtain a zygosity determination from cheek swabs is available from the MBF

continued over

Background

Zygosity Determination _{continued}

Parental response

In the MBF's experience some parents are disconcerted when the results of zygosity testing are not as they had anticipated. This can occur when they have mistakenly assumed that, because they can easily tell their children apart, they cannot be MZ. A few have needed the opportunity to discuss their feelings of confusion at some length.

A small minority of parents prefer not to know the zygosity of their children. The reason they often give is that the information will not affect the way they care for or bring up their children and they therefore do not wish their children to be 'labelled'.

Zygosity Determination continued

Parental response

- If the results are given to the parents by letter, ensure that:
    - both lay and technical terminology is used to avoid misunderstanding
    - the parents are given a contact person so that they can:
        - ask any questions
        - discuss any concerns
- If the results are given to the parents by telephone ensure that:
    - the information is fully understood
    - the messenger has the knowledge to answer questions and to discuss any concerns
- Where parents do not want to know the zygosity of their children, their wishes should be respected unless there are medical grounds for seeking to persuade them otherwise

Background

The Perinatal Period

This topic is covered much more fully in **Multiple Pregnancy**. Here we highlight those issues likely to have long-term implications for the children and their families.

All families with multiples deserve special help during the early months, or even early years.

Pregnancy

Close liaison between the various agencies concerned with the family's welfare is crucial from the time of diagnosis of a multiple pregnancy. Good antenatal preparation is also essential particularly with the growing trend towards early discharge from hospital (see **Multiple Pregnancy**). Mothers could often save many exhausting hours if they were given more practical advice on the day to day care of two babies. Too many learn by trial and error.

There is no doubt that emotional and practical support can best be provided by other mothers with multiple birth children. However, when a couple first hears that they are expecting twins or triplets, they may well not know another family in similar circumstances to whom they can turn for information and advice. They can feel very alone if they are not told that most areas in the UK now have a local parents of twins club, members of which are happy to make immediate contact with an expectant mother. The national Twins and Multiple Births Association (Tamba) provides a list of such clubs as well as literature (see FF106). Similar organisations exist in many other countries (a list is available on the MBF website).

Most people find it exhausting to care for two or more babies without adequate practical help and professional support. However, some mothers may have unrealistic expectations of parenthood, insist on trying to cope with their babies unaided and then feel especially guilty when they fail. Women who have for many years struggled to have a baby, constantly imagining themselves in a mother's role, often find it particularly hard as do those who have achieved high levels of success in intellectually demanding careers. Their problems may be exacerbated if prenatal preparation has been inadequate.

continued over

The Perinatal Period

Pregnancy

■ Family doctors should immediately pass on to a health visitor and community midwife full details of any woman expecting twins or more

■ At least one antenatal home visit should be made by the family doctor, midwife or health visitor as appropriate (See **Multiple Pregnancy**)

■ Hospital and community teams should:

  liaise with other agencies if necessary (e.g. housing, social services)

  ensure that couples expecting multiple births are:

  • made aware of the possibility of preterm delivery and encouraged to visit the hospital's neonatal unit

  • fully informed and adequately supported if any complications of pregnancy arise

  • given a realistic picture of parenting twins and more and, right from the start, encouraged to ask for support if they need it

  • adequately prepared for the practicalities of parenting (e.g. equipment, feeding, day-to-day management of the babies)

*(These points are all covered in detail in **Multiple Pregnancy**)*

continued over

Background

The Perinatal Period continued

Pregnancy continued

Some parents do not have the practical support of a relative or friend on a regular basis and will need additional help. If this has not been organised during the pregnancy and the mother becomes exhausted and overwrought, it is harder for both parents and professionals to organise help at short notice. It is much less difficult to cancel previously arranged help if it is not after all needed. There is no statutory obligation in the UK for Social Services to provide any additional help to families with multiples. In some cases it may be provided depending upon local resources. In many it is not. Failure to provide adequate support where it is required is a shortsighted approach. Appropriate help can go a long way towards reducing the risk of long-term problems which, when they occur, are more costly to resolve both in financial and emotional terms.

Buying equipment new - and in duplicate - may be unnecessary and expensive but parents often have no ready access to secondhand items. Mothers of twins may be poorly advised about what is likely to be the most useful.

Despite the many advantages of effective forward planning and the early purchase of specialist twin equipment such as prams, it should be noted that such items can also become a painful and expensive reminder should one baby be stillborn or die in the neonatal period. With the perinatal mortality rates being significantly higher with multiple births such an outcome is less uncommon than with single born babies. Some parents may prefer to reserve items, only taking delivery of them after both babies are safely home. Such an arrangement can often be organised with local stores.

Many parents consider names for their children during pregnancy. Although most are aware of the importance of encouraging individuality from the start, some are still tempted to give their babies 'twin' names, i.e. rhyming or like-sounding. Even the same initial can cause confusion later on, especially at school and with personal correspondence.

continued over

The Perinatal Period continued

Pregnancy continued

◼ Hospital and community teams should also:

liaise antenatally to develop a plan for preparing the family for life with twins. In particular, parents should be encouraged:

- to organise practical help in advance
- to keep in close contact with local Twins Clubs whose members can:
  - advise on types and sources of equipment as well as being a source of secondhand items
  - provide practical information and literature
  - become involved in parent education classes (see **Multiple Pregnancy**)
  - introduce parents to the local Twins Club and/or to individual families
  - visit mothers in hospital

encourage parents to consider readily distinguishable names for their babies emphasising the confusion that can otherwise arise

continued over

Background

The Perinatal Period continued

Newborn

In many cases, twins are born at or near term and require no special care. They are able to be with their mothers from the start and are ready to return home almost as soon as single born babies. However, because it is initially more difficult to breastfeed two babies than one, especially for primagravidas, mothers usually benefit from a longer hospital stay or more intensive help at home. Furthermore, most mothers will have had epidural anaesthesia and many an assisted delivery, making it difficult for them to meet the extra demands made by having to care for two babies simultaneously.

Because of the greater likelihood of preterm delivery and low birthweight among multiple births (with consequent relatively high levels of morbidity and perinatal mortality), a significant number of twins do, however, require neonatal care, sometimes for long periods. Any parent of a baby in intensive care experiences anguish and concern; in the case of twins and more, these emotions may be further complicated by having one healthy baby and one who is very ill - or even by one baby dying while the other still struggles to survive (see **Multiple Pregnancy**).

Although one baby may be ready to go home before the other, most units now try to postpone the discharge until both are strong enough unless it would mean the healthy baby spending many weeks or even months in hospital. The theory that it is easier to start with one baby alone seems to be ill-founded; it is harder to adapt to two babies if a routine with one has been established. Furthermore, if the mother is busy at home with one baby she may become increasingly attached to him as well as experiencing practical difficulties in visiting the other. Not only may the baby left in hospital suffer in his relationship with his mother but also in the development of his own self-esteem[6].

In hospital the mother of twins tends to be the centre of attention but she may not be prepared for the practical and emotional stresses that lie ahead. Many hours each day will be spent in the practical care of the babies but the effort involved can be significantly reduced by good organisation and the use of time saving techniques and equipment.

The Perinatal Period continued

Newborn

■ If one or both the babies are in neonatal care, the parents should be encouraged to spend as much time in the unit as possible

■ To make it as easy as possible for the parents to care for them, consider sending both babies to the unit if there is space, even if only one needs a cot for medical reasons

■ Breastfeeding mothers should be given consistent advice and support (see FF25)

■ Ensure that staff appreciate the need to treat twins as individuals and help the parents:

    to make their babies easily distinguishable

    to choose names for the babies and use them as soon as possible

■ Hospital staff should:

    refer to the babies by name

    encourage the family's health visitor to liaise with the neonatal unit as well as with the parents

    be sensitive to the conflicting emotions that the parents may experience, especially if one baby is much iller than the other, and provide appropriate support

■ Whenever possible keep the babies together until both are well enough to return home

■ If separation is unavoidable, staff should:

    encourage the mother to visit

    ensure that:

        • a nursery and feeds are available for the second baby so that he can accompany the mother to the hospital

        • older siblings are included so that they are not further separated from their mother

Background

The Early Months

Coping at home

On returning home, the new mother of twins may feel both physically and emotionally daunted by the prospect of caring for two babies. This is particularly likely if she has suffered obstetric complications. Parents who have conceived twins or more as a result of treatment for infertility may feel under extra pressure to cope. Many years of childlessness can create high, even unrealistic, expectations of parenthood. Moreover, some misguidedly feel they have 'brought upon themselves' any practical difficulties they may be experiencing. They may therefore be especially reluctant to admit that they are finding life hard - not least because they are in general less likely to get a sympathetic response[7] than those who have spontaneously conceived their babies.

Most new mothers of twins suffer from lack of sleep[8] with consequent chronic fatigue[9]. Indeed, exhaustion is the most common complaint from mothers of twins and this is likely to be a major contributing factor to both the depression and anxiety that have been shown to be more common in this group[1]. It is also worrying to find that depression may well continue for some years beyond the period of acute fatigue[10].

In addition, many women feel guilty that they are able to give so little attention to their partner and, particularly the houseproud, that they cannot maintain previously high standards in running their home. Many such couples paint a deceptively rosy picture of their domestic situation and it is only on visiting the family at home that the full stress is revealed - and even then it may not be readily acknowledged by the parents.

Multiple birth babies, given their probable prematurity, are more likely to require medical follow-up often over several years. It is logistically extremely difficult for one parent to take the babies to the surgery or health centre. Not only is it a challenge to get the babies there, especially on public transport, but on arrival it is hard to look after them in the waiting area because prams and pushchairs often have to be left outside. In addition, it is not uncommon for two or three babies to be given one appointment between them all.

Isolation is a problem for many, with mothers of very young twins tending to leave the house only half as often as those with single babies[11]. This is often due to practical difficulties. Many mothers do not have access to a car during the day. Travel by public transport is very difficult with two babies and when there is a toddler sibling it may become impossible. Even shopping locally with the babies may present problems such as doors too narrow for double buggies or lack of functioning lifts in apartment blocks.

continued over

The Early Months

Coping at home

■ Families with twins must be identified as having high priority need of home visits by community midwives and health visitors

■ Extra visits must be made in the early days to ensure that the mother is:

   breastfeeding successfully

   getting sufficient rest

   receiving adequate help

   able to get out of the house with or without the babies to:

   • do the shopping

   • attend clinics (where necessary)

   • maintain social contact

   not creating unnecessary work for herself (e.g. daily baths for the babies)

■ Home visits should be made whenever possible, especially for weighing

■ If practice policy permits, trained health visitors should consider doing home immunisations

■ If practice policy does not allow immunisation by health visitors, then the family doctor should try to make a home visit to immunise the babies

■ Visits to the surgery or health centre should be facilitated by one or more of the following:

   allowing prams to be brought into the waiting area

   ensuring that, if the mother comes alone, someone is available to hold the second baby

   giving a double appointment for two babies

   seeing and assessing each baby on his own

   making special arrangements for the family (e.g. giving an appointment before the main surgery/clinic starts)

continued over

Background

The Early Months continued

Coping at home continued

Lack of social contact can further add to any feelings of depression. Many mothers complain of the isolation they feel during the first year. Often family and friends rally round for the first two or three months. Help may then suddenly dwindle leaving the mothers alone during a period of great stress and fatigue.

Not surprisingly, mothers of twins spend less time with each baby than they would if they only had one[12]. In addition, they have very little time to 'enjoy' their babies, because the practical demands of caring for them are so great[13]. The traditional image of motherhood portrays parenting one baby at a time and mothers with multiples may feel deprived of this experience and frustrated by their inability to give undivided attention to each child.

However, parents may be reluctant to remedy this situation by separating the twins even for short periods. Some feel that the children themselves have emotional bonds that must not be broken in this way; others find separation hard to organise for practical reasons; some may even feel that by letting someone else look after one of the babies their 'special' status as a twin parent may be diminished or their competence questioned.

The MBF's experience would suggest that separation can become increasingly difficult the longer it is postponed and that later relationships between the twins themselves and with other people can also be affected. The MBF has seen many examples of adult twins handicapped both by their dependency on each other and by their inability to function happily apart from their twin.

Some mothers cope remarkably well in the early months, especially if they have adequate help and undemanding babies and are able to establish a routine early on. In cases like this, it is tempting to assume that they no longer require extra health visitor support. However, in the MBF's experience, such families sometimes find the emotional demands of the toddler/pre-school stage unexpectedly difficult.

Too often parents of multiples strive to live up to the "happy family" image they feel is expected of them and professionals may sometimes fail to appreciate the underlying strain. Others who have confessed to their feelings of exhaustion, inadequacy and a need for help have been met by nothing more than reassurance that they are coping perfectly well. Such a reaction can be very distressing.

continued over

The Early Months continued

Coping at home continued

▪ Help the mother to avoid isolation by:

- recommending suitable prams and pushchairs

- suggesting other modes of transport (e.g. one sling and one pushchair)

- encouraging her to get out when possible, both alone and with her partner

- seeking help from a neighbour (e.g. a teenager) for outings

▪ The benefits of sometimes separating the babies from an early age should be clearly explained

▪ The mother should be encouraged to arrange regular times when she can be alone with one baby so that she can:

- give her undivided attention to one baby

- develop a close relationship with each baby as an individual

- increase her enjoyment of each baby

- lessen the frustration of interrupted mothering

- promote the individuality of each twin from the start

- give the babies experience of being on their own

▪ Any mother who expresses feelings of exhaustion or inability to cope should always be taken seriously

continued over

Background

The Early Months continued

One parent families

An increasing number of twins are being brought up by one parent, usually the mother. Many lone parents, particularly those who are able to establish a regular routine from the start, cope remarkably well. Inevitably, however, the pressures are considerable particularly in times of illness. The main stresses are usually those caused by fatigue and isolation. Having sole care, night and day, of two babies is exhausting and those with other small children who may need taking to nursery or school can find the situation almost impossible. Many, particularly those living in high rise accommodation, cannot leave the house without the help of a second adult. Others find the lack of adult companionship and being alone with two young children for 24 hours a day the most difficult to handle.

Housing

Parents do not plan to have more than one child at once. Consequently, the arrival of two or more children may result in their accommodation becoming unexpectedly inadequate. Moreover, a multiple birth may mean that they are financially less able than they would otherwise have been to remedy the situation. Problems can arise not only with physically accommodating the family but also with taking the children out - especially for those living on upper storeys. Even where there is a lift, it may be too small to carry an adult with a double or triple buggy. It is simply not possible to carry two or more children, especially as they get older and heavier, plus a folded pushchair - not to mention other items such as shopping.

Because of the high mortality rate local authorities often refuse to rehouse multiple birth families before the babies are born or indeed are ready to come home. This can cause additional strain. Moreover, the "points" traditionally awarded per child over a number of years and (according to which housing places are usually allocated) often do not take into account the urgent need for additional space caused by the arrival of twins or more.

continued over

The Early Months continued

One parent families

■ It is important to establish during the pregnancy (or when the parent first is on their own):

  ▪ what reliable support is or will be available from family and friends

  ▪ whether her housing circumstances are such that the mother is able to get the babies out unaided

  ▪ that the mother has contact details for the local parents of twins club and of the Tamba One Parent Families Group (see FF107)

  ▪ what help, if any, will be available in times of emergency (e.g. if mother is ill or one child has to go into hospital)

Housing

■ Housing should be discussed once a multiple pregnancy is well established with regard to:

  ▪ size

  ▪ accessibility (i.e. will the mother be able to take the babies out unaided)

■ If necessary, the housing department should be contacted as early as possible and the special needs for families with multiples emphasised

■ Wherever possible, the family should be re-housed during pregnancy or at least well before any preterm babies come home from hospital

■ Accommodation should have a safe play area, ideally its own garden

continued over

Background

Feeding[M]

Establishing the easiest and most satisfactory means of feeding two or more infants is vital to the happiness of mother and babies alike. Special preparation and ongoing support are essential for this to happen. The need for specific antenatal preparation for feeding twins is outlined in **Multiple Pregnancy**.

Breastfeeding

Many twins have been fully and happily breastfed and have thrived[14]. A few mothers have even produced enough milk for three babies[15] but the majority who breastfeed triplets, combine breast and bottle. Twins, and triplets even more so, are a vulnerable group, likely to be preterm and of low birthweight. The benefits of breast milk are therefore particularly great.

Despite their innate ability, many mothers of twins are still discouraged, even dissuaded, from breastfeeding on the mistaken assumption that milk supply will be inadequate and maternal exhaustion inevitable. Lack of practical support and conflicting advice combine to result in high drop out rates during the early weeks.

There have still been relatively few studies of feeding patterns in twins but an early study[16] reported that the breastfed babies gained weight satisfactorily. The estimated daily food supplementation needed by a lactating mother is 500-600 kcal *per baby*[17]. The extra nutrition can be provided by relatively cheap foods and the costs of these need amount to no more than one third of that of formula milk.

The benefits of breast feeding are well documented. They include nutritional, immunological, psychological, practical and economic advantages. For twin babies these are increased because prematurity makes them more vulnerable to infection; physical contact is greater - two babies cannot be easily held and bottle fed together; a substantial amount of time and money, always in shorter supply than with a single baby, can be saved.

The most obvious disadvantage of breast feeding is that the mother can have no respite during the early months. She will therefore need strategies that allow an occasional uninterrupted night or infant-free outing, so that she does not become too tired and demoralised. After the first 14 days, the ability to express and store frozen milk can significantly extend the time babies are breastfed if difficulties arise.

continued over

Feeding^M

See **Multiple Pregnancy** for details of specific antenatal preparation for mothers of twins

Mothers should be introduced to the local twins group for practical advice and support pre- and postnatally

Breastfeeding

- Close liaison should be established between hospital and community staff including health visitors to ensure consistency of advice and support

- Everyone should use the same feeding policy, which must include specific provision for multiple births

- Reassure the mother that some breast milk, for however short a time, is much better than none at all

- Provide or arrange for readily available advice from a breastfeeding counsellor who has knowledge of the problems experienced by mothers of twins

- Ensure (or stress the need for) continuous hands-on help and encouragement throughout each feed, until breastfeeding is well established

continued over

Background

Feeding continued

Breastfeeding continued

Together or apart?

There are advantages to both methods and the mother will soon discover which suits her best.

There is some suggestion that prolactin production is enhanced if babies are suckled simultaneously[18]. Furthermore if one baby has a poor suck initially, the force of his brother's suck may produce a let down reflex in the other breast, providing milk to the weaker twin with less sucking effort on his part. However, new mothers often find it easier to breastfeed the babies separately in the first few days especially if they are preterm.

If they are fed separately, the mother can give her full concentration to each and she may find that she is generally more comfortable. However, feeds will then take up much of the day and the mother may also be distressed by the crying of the other baby. There is of course no reason why she should not vary her practice to what suits her and the babies best at the time. It is theoretically better to alternate who is fed first. In practice one baby may always demand the first feed. Either way, each baby should be offered one breast only at a feed to ensure that one does not receive all the foremilk with its lower fat content.

The main advantage of feeding the babies together is the time saved. In addition, some mothers find that it is actually more comfortable if both breasts are emptying at the same time, rather than feeling tension (and leaking) in the unsuckled breast - a bonus that mothers of single born babies cannot enjoy!

Establishing breastfeeding

This can sometimes be difficult for a mother with one full term baby. It is therefore not surprising that many mothers of twins find the early days of breastfeeding a frustrating struggle. Without continuous help, securely latching both babies (particularly if preterm) onto the breasts can be an insuperable challenge. The problems are obviously magnified if the mother is exhausted or lacking in guidance[19] and encouragement or feels pressurised to conform to an inflexible ward routine.

Many feeding positions have been devised. Most mothers stick to one but others vary their practice according to circumstance. Some women find that the babies are happier on the same side each time (possibly regulating their own supply of milk) but the majority prefer to change at each feed and have ingenious methods of remembering who is due for which breast.

continued over

Feeding continued

Breastfeeding continued

Together or apart?

■ Inform the mother that feeding her babies together may stimulate milk production in the early days[18]

■ <u>But</u> advise her that:

   the most important thing is that she feel confident in handling her babies and that feeding them one at a time at least initially may suit her better

   once feeding is well established she should adopt the method (one or two babies at a time) and positioning that suits her best

■ For those who wish to alternate breasts, suggest ways that mothers may be reminded which baby is due for which breast (e.g. safety pin on bra strap)

■ If she has not already learned antenatally, teach the mother to express milk and to save some in the freezer

Establishing breastfeeding

■ Ensure that:

   support is provided to multigravidas, however experienced they may be in breastfeeding single babies

   the mother's breastfeeding counsellor liaises with the health visitor

■ Continue to reassure the mother that establishing full breastfeeding may take several weeks

■ Encourage the mother to give herself time off by allowing others to feed the babies with stored expressed breast milk

continued over

Background

Feeding continued

Breastfeeding continued

Establishing breastfeeding continued

Demand feeding is less easy to practice with twins than a single baby and many mothers find that the most practical method is to feed both babies when one has indicated that he is hungry.

If the milk supply remains inadequate some mothers may choose to alternate between bottlefeeding one twin and breastfeeding the other at each feed. Occasionally a mother chooses to entirely breastfeed one baby and bottlefeed the other, either because one is frailer or because the other refuses to suckle. If this occurs the mother is likely to spend more time and may therefore develop a closer relationship with the breastfed baby.

Bottlefeeding

The most obvious advantage of bottlefeeding twins is that the task can be shared. In particular, the father is able to feel involved in this key aspect of caring for the babies. In addition, the mother may find it less physically demanding.

As well as the immunological aspects, the disadvantages of bottlefeeding include the increased cost, greater amount of work in sterilising bottles and making up feeds, the fridge space required for storing a large number of bottles and, most importantly, the mother's inability to nurse and feed both babies simultaneously.

Weaning

Mothers are sometimes placed under unnecessary pressure to wean their babies from the breast, both by healthcare professionals and relatives. Extended breastfeeding is particularly valuable for twins as it ensures a continuing physical closeness with the mother which, in the time-consuming business of caring for her babies, is often difficult to achieve in other ways. There is no reason why twins (particularly DZ) should be ready to wean at the same time. Left to their own inclinations, the babies may well choose to do so several weeks apart.

Introducing solid foods to twin babies is an added task so mothers are often relieved if this can be postponed for as long as possible, at least until four months of age and, for babies (especially the breastfed) who are content to wait, until six months. It is generally accepted that prematurity need not be taken into account when considering the introduction of solids.

continued over

Feeding continued

Breastfeeding continued

Establishing breastfeeding continued

- Encourage the mother to develop a feeding routine - responding to the first baby's demand and waking the second to feed at the same time or immediately afterwards is often the most satisfactory arrangement

- If only one baby is being breastfed, encourage the mother to spend some time during the day alone with the bottlefed baby

Bottlefeeding

- Ensure that, before she leaves hospital, the mother:

    - has the necessary equipment at home for two babies

    - knows how to sterilise and make up feeds in quantity

Weaning

- Encourage the mother:

    - to postpone weaning each baby until it becomes clear that he is no longer satisfied by milk alone

    - to be prepared for one twin to be weaned before the other

    - to make the process as straightforward as possible by:

        - simplifying the kitchen routine

        - making and freezing purees in quantity or buying in bulk

        - positioning children so that they can easily be fed at the same time

        - considering feeding from a single bowl and spoon

continued over

Background

Feeding continued

Weaning continued

Many mothers find it best to sit the babies in chairs side by side and to feed each by turn with one spoon from one bowl. Parents tend to assume that both babies will have the same nutritional needs. This is not always the case, particularly where they are of different sex and/or birthweight.

Childhood

When the children begin to take a more active part they can have their own bowls and spoons whilst their mother continues to provide the bulk of the food from the communal source. Because a busy mother is less likely to give her children the time to experiment, many twins are slow in learning to feed themselves. Exploration with food and the process of feeding is an important part of a child's development.

Parents of twins may assume that they will have the same taste in foods and similar appetites. However, this is often not the case. In the same way, both children may not be hungry or thirsty at the same moment.

All parents are concerned for their children's satisfactory nutrition. Sensing this concern, some children use the process of eating, or refusal to do so, as a means of gaining parental attention. This is even more common in twins who must constantly compete for such attention.

Feeding continued

Childhood

◼ Encourage the mother:

    to welcome the children's participation, as soon as they are ready, by:

- providing each with his own spoon and bowl (ideally with a suction pad beneath)
- providing space and plastic floor covering to simplify the subsequent clean-up
- giving them only small amounts of food in their bowls
- praising their efforts
- ignoring attention seeking activities
- ensuring that mealtimes are not unnecessarily prolonged

◼ Parents should be made aware that their twins are no more likely than single born siblings to:

    have the same likes and dislikes

    be hungry or thirsty at the same time

    want exactly the same amount of food

◼ When meal times are disrupted or protracted parents should consider:

    having clear limits as to when behaviour is unacceptable

    limiting the length of the meal (regardless of whether the food has been eaten)

    separating the children

Background

Sleep^M

One of the most common problems faced by parents of multiples is how to get the babies into a satisfactory sleep pattern. The endurance of the mother and the happiness of the whole family can ultimately depend on this. Yet many parents have in retrospect blamed themselves for allowing unnecessarily troublesome sleep patterns to develop in their twins.

Not only can two wakeful babies take turns to disrupt but the crying of one may disturb the other and then each reinforce the other's distress. Multiple birth infants may be slower to establish a satisfactory routine due to their prematurity, need for frequent feeds and their experience of constant attention and broken sleep on the neonatal unit. Furthermore, mothers often reinforce bad sleeping habits by responding immediately to the cries of one baby to prevent the other being disturbed. The children may quickly take advantage of this easily won attention.

An added stress may arise from older siblings who, resentful of the attention diverted to the baby twins, may seek extra attention and cuddles by not settling at night.

There is no simple answer to sleep problems.

continued over

Sleep^M

Many of the sleep problems affecting families with twins and ways of solving them are the same as those for single born children. Advice can only be given after careful exploration of the individual family's circumstances and attitudes.

Antenatal

■ Help parents to consider where the babies may best sleep:

  in the same cot

  in the same room

  in their parents' room

The first six months

■ If the babies are on the neonatal unit, the staff should discuss with the parents how best to establish a routine at home taking into account the frequent feeds that may be necessary with preterm babies

■ Emphasise to parents the importance of:

  following national healthcare guidelines for the positioning of babies in their cots

  checking that the babies do not get too warm, particularly if they are sharing a cot

  establishing a regular routine as soon as possible

  ensuring that all those involved with the care of the babies are consistent in their approach with regard to sleep

■ Encourage the parents from the start to:

  go through the same bedtime routine every night

  leave the changing area ready and fully equipped for the next time

  put the babies down to sleep at regular times during the day in their bedroom

continued over

Background

Sleep continued

Early sleeping arrangements will depend on many factors including the space available, the room temperature and the sleeping patterns of each of the babies. Whether the babies share a cot or even a room will depend on these as well the parents' inclinations.

Cot sharing is an issue which many parents want to consider for the comfort of their babies as well as convenience. Theoretical disadvantages of co-bedding, apart from disturbing each other, are the risks of overheating or suffocation and thus of Sudden Infant Death Syndrome (SIDS). As yet there has been only very limited research on which to base guidance. But there is currently nothing to suggest an increase in SIDS in co-bedded twins. Indeed, it has been suggested that there may be benefits to such a sleeping arrangement with the babies providing reciprocal support to each other through a co-regulation developed during intrauterine life.

It has been shown that co-bedded preterm twins move closer together, touch one another, are awake at the same time and, by their physical proximity to each other, reduce the amount of extra room heating needed[20]. In addition, there is at least anecdotal evidence that such physical contact with each other can reduce the frequency of apnoeic episodes in some preterm pairs. There has also been one report of more settled sleep patterns and more rapid weight gain during the first months[21].

During the early months a cot can be satisfactorily divided across the middle with one baby sleeping at either end, their feet touching the partition to ensure that they don't wriggle down under the covers. Later, when they are in separate cots, some babies are comforted by being close enough to touch each other and may, on waking, resettle on their own. Others disturb each other and are better well separated, possibly even in different rooms.

continued over

Sleep continued

The first six months continued

- Encourage the parents from the start to:
    - resist the temptation to lift the baby as soon as he cries so that he does not come to associate crying with being picked up
    - avoid turning the main light on during the night - a night light may be useful
- While the babies still require night time feeds the mother should be encouraged to:
    - consider waking the babies just before going to bed
    - consider waking the second baby when the first is hungry
    - have a drink for herself in a jug or thermos by her bedside or wherever she will be feeding

Six months and beyond

- Encourage parents to:
    - avoid exciting the children before bedtime
    - give each child a separate bath or bedtime story if two adults are available
    - put each child in his bed while he is still awake
    - provide each child with his own soft toy or comforter which he never has to share
    - resist the temptation to:
        - rock or cuddle the children to sleep .
        - linger in the room after goodnight has been said
- If the children are waking each other, parents should be encouraged to consider:
    - separate rooms, where feasible (a travel cot can be put temporarily in another room, preferably not the parents' bedroom)
    - placing the better sleeper with an older sibling

continued over

Background

Sleep continued

By six months a routine should have been established. Inevitably, more attention may be demanded if one baby is unwell or teething or there has been some other disturbance, such as a house move. However, if the normal routine is not resumed reasonably quickly, bad habits may become entrenched and be difficult to change.

It is often assumed that if there are several children in the family the twins should always sleep together. However, some parents have found that the nights are less disturbed if a twin shares with one of the other siblings.

Whether twins should share a room or not will, of course, depend on the size of the house and the inclinations of the parents and children. Most children benefit from at least having their own territory from the start with their own chest or shelf and wall space.

If available, twin children often enjoy having their own bedroom in which they can keep their own possessions. They may like the choice, at least initially, to sleep together. A second bed or mattress in one room can leave this option open.

Sleep continued

Six months and beyond continued

- If poor sleeping patterns have developed, encourage the parents to:

  - identify the problem(s) by keeping a sleep diary for each child

  - gradually bring forward the bedtime by 15 minutes until the required time is reached

  - practice a 'gradual withdrawal' for children who are used to having a parent present until they sleep

  - refrain from attending to the child at the first cry

  - avoid taking the children into bed with them (where older children are used to coming into the parental bed, a mattress on the floor can be a first step towards ending the habit especially if parents are too tired to return them to their own beds)

  - consider a 'controlled crying programme'[M] which should only be instituted:

    - with the agreement of both parents

    - with the firm resolve to carry it through

    - when there is opportunity for the parent(s) to catch up on lost sleep during the day

- If the mother and/or father are becoming exhausted consider:

  - providing a night-time carer for one or two nights per week

  - providing help in the day to allow mother a few hours rest

  - encouraging parents to see if a relative or friend might have one child to stay overnight (a non parent adult can often break a poor sleeping pattern)

- Each child should be encouraged to have an area (whether in a shared room or separate) which he can arrange in his own way and call his own. If the twins are in separate rooms, a spare bed or mattress in one will allow them to sleep together if they wish whilst allowing each to retain his own territory.

Background

Physical Growth

Birthweight

Multiple birth babies are likely to be of low birthweight due to a combination of preterm delivery and intrauterine growth retardation. Just over 50 per cent of multiple births in the UK weigh less than 2500g compared to six per cent of singletons. Nearly 10 per cent weigh less than 1500g compared with one per cent of singletons[22]. Whatever the number of fetuses, it seems that all grow at a rate similar to that of singletons until the latter part of the second trimester of pregnancy. Only then does growth slow down in direct relation to the number of fetuses that the uteroplacental circulation must supply (see **Multiple Pregnancy**).

These factors mean that many of the infants, particularly the more mature, are light for their gestational age when compared with single born babies. As with singletons, male twins tend to be slightly heavier than females. The birthweight of twins is unrelated to birth order.

Growth in childhood

The most comprehensive data on growth in twins continues to come from the ongoing Louisville Twins Study[23]. By four years the twins had caught up in height with singletons but remained lighter. This same pattern has been found by others in older twins[24] and in intrauterine growth retarded children in general. However, there was a small group of twins who had been very light for dates (below the 5th centile) at birth who remained of short stature[24].

Few studies have considered the effect of zygosity on growth but it appears that adult MZ twins are slightly smaller than DZ[25]. This could be due to genetic influences. Mothers of DZ twins are on average taller than MZ (see **Facts about Multiple Births**).

In intrauterine life the environment of one fetus may be very different from that of his co-twin, particularly in those monochorionic pairs with the fetofetal transfusion syndrome. MZ twins who have been affected by this condition are often different sizes at birth and this difference may persist. Why some smaller MZ twins should show such a remarkable ability to catch up whilst others remain permanently smaller is uncertain. It may be related to the timing of the nutritional deprivation and its effect on the cellular composition of the body and therefore of the growth potential.

continued over

Physical Growth

Birthweight and growth in childhood

- Birth measurements should be recorded on charts appropriate for twins[26] where these are available as well as standard ones

- The length, weight and occipito frontal circumference of all twins should be measured regularly from birth and recorded on centile charts

- Light for dates children should have long-term monitoring of their growth

- Parents should be discouraged from comparing the rates of growth in DZ twins and reminded that their pattern of physical development can vary as widely as that between any singleton siblings

continued over

Background

Physical Growth continued

Growth in childhood continued

If growth in MZ twins becomes discordant later a reason should always be sought and causes such as chronic infection or hormone deficiency considered. The growth of DZ twins need not be any more similar than that of single born siblings.

After birth, genetic influences dictate differences in growth pattern and, through childhood, the growth of MZ twins generally becomes increasingly concordant whereas that of DZ pairs becomes less[27]. Pronounced discordancy may irritate or even distress the smaller twin particularly since his lack of height may result in people believing he is a younger brother. Unlike DZ twins, MZ children tend to have similar growth patterns, coinciding their periods of acceleration and latency.

As girls on average start puberty two years ahead of boys, the girl in unlike sex pairs may be several inches taller than her brother in the early teenage years. Even in DZ like sex twins the onset of puberty can be several years apart. The earlier growth spurt in one may mean a reversal or substantial discrepancy in their heights as well as their sexual development. The smaller twin sometimes finds this period emotionally stressful.

The use of steroid therapy (e.g. for asthma) can affect growth. With a single born child this may pass unnoticed. However, such a side effect may be much more apparent where one twin is receiving treatment and the other is not. The affected child will often make up some or all of the deficit when the medication stops.

A more subtle cause of growth discordancy in twins could be emotional or physical neglect of one of the children.

Physical Growth continued

Growth in childhood continued

■ Parents and teachers should be aware of the emotional stresses and needs of the smaller twin, not least during puberty

■ In MZ twins, discordant growth should lead to further investigation including both physical and psychosocial causes if:

  ■ the infants/children were previously similarly sized

  ■ the difference in height or weight centiles in those discordant from birth has increased

■ The growth of twins on steroid therapy should be carefully monitored. In MZ pairs, the possibility of growth affecting medication should always be considered if their rates of growth become discordant

Background

Development

Because of the higher risk of low birthweight and preterm delivery, twins are more likely to suffer from neonatal complications that can lead to long-term neurodevelopmental problems. However, contrary to popular belief, once they have made up any deficit due to preterm birth, the overall development of the great majority of twins is similar to that of singleton children. The one exception to this is language development (see FF46).

MZ twins tend to develop at a similar rate with concordant lags and spurts[28]. Any significant discrepancy is a cause for concern. However, DZ twins may not only show the wide range of intellectual and motor abilities seen in any family but it is also recognised that they may accelerate or pause at different times, resulting on occasion in marked discordancy. Even though the development of both may be well within normal limits, this discrepancy can cause understandable (if unnecessary) parental concern and can also be disconcerting for the slower twin.

Sometimes, however, justifiable parental anxiety is ignored and a problem mistakenly attributed solely to the twinship. This may then result in delayed recognition of an underlying disorder.

When twins are of very different sizes, some parents have unjustifiably high expectations of the larger twin's development even if the smaller one has been fit and well from the start. They may assume for instance that the larger child will walk first and expect other skills to be more advanced, even when those are unrelated to strength (e.g. speech).

The increased risk of depression in mothers of preschool twins[10] could be a further factor in any apparent delay as it is well recognised that maternal emotional well-being has a significant influence on the development of children[29].

The development of all children is also affected by the opportunities available to them. For reasons of both safety and time and the havoc that two can cause, many multiple birth children may be deprived of experiences and stimulation which a single born child routinely enjoys. Once they reach the crawling and, even more so, the toddling stage, they may spend more time confined to playpens and cots, missing out on early exploration. For speed, a mother may feed and dress the children long beyond an age when they would normally be expected to manage on their own - with repercussions (particularly with regard to the children's ability to dress themselves) that may extend into nursery or even primary school. Activities such as cooking, sand and water play may lead to such mess and conflict that early attempts are abandoned. Even outings to the playground or shops may be limited. Later, some activities such as swimming that cannot be undertaken without a second adult may also prove too difficult.

continued over

Development

- The development of twins should be monitored from birth
- Measurements should be made against those of single born peers of the same gestational age
- Each child should be examined and assessed individually
- The behaviour and play of the children should be observed together and apart
- Significant discrepancy in development of MZ twins should be investigated
- Parental anxiety should always be taken seriously and appropriate investigations instigated
- In children of discordant size, parents may need to be reminded that there is no reason why the larger twin should be more developmentally advanced or socially mature than the smaller
- Maternal depression should always be considered in cases where there is no other obvious cause for slow development in a child
- Stress to parents the importance of teaching their children to be independent
- Encourage parents:
  - to allow sufficient time for the children to dress and feed themselves whenever possible
  - to arrange the house so that children can:
    - have the opportunity for exploration
    - freely enjoy messy play (e.g. sand, water, finger paints)
  - to consider having one room where the children can safely play on their own
  - to arrange to have a second adult for outings

continued over

Background

Development continued

Mirror imaging

MZ twins can be mirror images of each other, which means that they have some degree of asymmetry and/or the reversal of superficial features, including hair whorls and tooth eruption. They may have opposite handedness.

In its most complete manifestation some or all the internal organs may also be reversed (situs inversus). However, this is rare and, of the internal organs, the heart is the most commonly affected[30].

Asymmetry probably arises from the late division of the embryo when the left and right sides have already been determined[31].

Laterality

The reported frequency of left-handedness is more common in twins and has varied widely from 5 to 31 per cent. There is even disagreement as to whether there is a difference in frequency between MZ and DZ twins[30].

There may well be three separate populations of left-handed children. One of these groups would be genetically determined and hence no more common amongst twins than singletons. The second 'pathological' group would be that of children whose left-handedness is a result of damage to the normally dominant left cerebral hemisphere during the intrauterine or perinatal periods. This group is certainly likely to be disproportionately represented amongst multiple birth children because of the greater likelihood of preterm birth and the complications that this can cause, including intraventricular haemorrhage. The third group will be limited to MZ twins and associated with mirror imaging.

continued over

Development continued

Mirror imaging

■ Signs of mirror imaging in MZ twins should be sought, such as:

- opposite handedness
- reversal of:
    - superficial features (e.g. hair whorls)
    - eruption pattern and formation of teeth
    - the heart (dextrocardia)
    - other internal organs (situs inversus)

Laterality

■ Assessment of a left-handed twin child should include:

- a family history of left-handedness
- a history of perinatal complications
- a full neurological examination
- an examination, in MZ twins, for other signs of mirror imaging

continued over

Background

Development continued

Language

Many studies in the past have shown that twins, particularly boys, are slower in their language development than singletons[32-36]. For triplets the problems may be greater still[37]. Furthermore, delay in language development in the preschool period is more likely to result in reading difficulties later on[38] as well as attention disorders[39], even though most catch up in their language skills by the time they reach school[40]. There are a number of reasons why multiple birth children are at risk of language delay and many of these can be prevented if addressed early.

Language delay is neither inevitable nor irremediable but too often treatment is delayed because professionals assume that poor speech is acceptable (or even inevitable) in twins. But it has been well demonstrated that affected twins can improve dramatically with appropriate help, particularly when treatment is instigated at an early age – and certainly no later than it would have been in a single child displaying similar signs of delay.

The causes of speech delay are probably a combination of the adverse perinatal factors and the differences in the postnatal environment experienced by twins compared to singletons[2]. Twins have to develop a much more complicated form of interaction right from the start. Unlike single born children (even those with a sibling), they have constantly to communicate within a threesome (an adult and their twin) and to do so effectively requires much more complex speaking and listening skills.

Verbal interaction of all kinds appears to be reduced in families with twins and there are often few opportunities for one to one communication. Indeed, it has been shown that mothers of twins not only talk less to their children[41] but that they tend to use shorter and grammatically less complex sentences. Moreover mothers may mistakenly believe that there is less need to talk to their children because twins entertain each other. They also tend to give fewer suggestions or explanations and less praise.

In the constant competition for attention and because an adult physically cannot maintain eye contact with two children simultaneously, one twin may receive more language input than the other. The more determined child may become the spokesman for the pair and the other only induced to speak when his twin is not there.

continued over

Development continued

Language

- Parents and professionals must never assume that twins will be delayed in their speech and language development

- Parents should be encouraged to promote their children's language development by:

    - talking to them as much as possible

    - giving each twin periods of one to one communication with an adult from the start

    - making eye contact with the child to whom they are speaking

    - speaking and directing questions to one child at a time

    - ensuring that they do not unintentionally always address the same child because he is more responsive than his twin

    - ensuring that one twin does not answer for the other or act as spokesman for the pair

    - allowing each child the opportunity to tell his own story at his own pace and without interruption

    - reading regularly to each twin separately

    - playing with toys that encourage description (e.g. dolls house, farmyard)

    - ensuring that the twins play separately with older, linguistically more advanced children

    - offering a full explanation – to each child if necessary

    - giving encouragement and praise

- If a child is slow to speak:

    - arrange for hearing to be checked

    - advise the parents:

        - to increase the time the child spends alone with an adult

        - on means of stimulating speech in the child

        - to arrange for each twin to spend periods separately with another child(ren) (e.g. at playschool or by 'swapping' one twin from another pair)

    - consider a referral for further assessment

continued over

Background

Development continued

Language continued

Cryptophasia or idioglossia, the 'secret language' of twins, is a language incomprehensible to others. Exclusive cryptophasia is extremely rare but many twins have it alongside normal language. Incidences of up to 40 per cent have been reported, with a higher incidence amongst MZ twins in some studies[42,43]. Cryptophasia is not in itself a problem if normal language skills are developing at the same time.

The advantages of being bilingual are obvious and there is no evidence to suggest that twins suffer from exposure to two languages at the same time. Most bilingual families give careful thought to how best to compensate for any confusion or other detrimental effects that may arise.

Stuttering

There has been little work on stuttering in twins but there is some evidence that it is slightly more common than in singletons[44]. This is not surprising in view of the stress experienced by a young child who constantly has to compete to get his word in first. It can be particularly upsetting for the twin that stutters if his brother has no difficulty in expressing himself. This is not only frustrating but may also be humiliating when the inevitable comparisons are made. By the same token, although the principles of management of a twin child who stutters should be no different to that of a singleton, they may in practice be more difficult to implement because uninterrupted one to one communication is much harder to achieve. Although long term problems with stuttering are rare, parents of twins may be in special need of reassurance and advice on management.

continued over

Development continued

Language continued

■ If a twin child is slow to reach the stage of language development expected in a single born child (in comprehension or expression), professional advice should be sought immediately. Twinship in itself should never be a reason to delay assessment, investigation or intervention

■ The children should always be assessed separately and out of sight and earshot of their twin

■ Although all assessments and treatments should be given separately, the behaviour and language of the children when they are together should also be observed to see if:

  one child is always the spokesperson

  the children have their own 'twin' language and other forms of communication

■ If the children are to be bilingual, parents should ensure that either:

  any particular adult always speaks to the children in the same language

  they use one language at home and the second when they are out

  they consider concentrating on one language if a child is showing signs of language delay

Stuttering

■ Ignore the problem as much as possible

■ Ensure that the children take turns when talking

■ Give the children time apart in order to:

  avoid comparisons

  provide a setting in which the affected child:

  • can feel able to speak unhurriedly

  • can have a one to one conversation with an adult

  • is encouraged to use descriptive language during activities (e.g. drawing, interactive and creative play)

■ Consider early referral to a speech therapist

continued over

Background

Development continued

Personality and identity

Personality differences in twins are often apparent from a very early age, even in MZ twins although they tend to be more similar in their behaviour than DZ pairs[45]. In the early years the differences between the children tend to manifest themselves more in temper and attention span, whereas a variance in the degree of sociability is more common in older twins.

Some twins are very conscious of which of them was born first. Birth order has been shown to be one of the factors that later determines a twin's self esteem[6] and may lead to the first born having the traits characteristic of the eldest child in the family[46] such as leadership skills and aggression. This result may, in part at least, be due to the disproportionate interest in birth order so frequently shown by other people.

In the past, twin children were often treated as a single unit, dressed alike, rarely separated from each other and frequently given twin-sounding names. Although less prevalent today, these tendencies still exist especially with regard to naming. Even having the same initial can be a disadvantage to a teenager, especially in relation to school work and personal correspondence.

If the babies are dressed the same, it makes it even more difficult for people to tell them apart, use their correct names and treat them as individuals. Although most parents now appreciate the importance of the children developing their own identities, external pressures (not least from grandparents) may make it difficult for them to carry out their intentions of dressing their twins differently. Some parents who initially dress their children alike plan to change later but patterns set in the first year can be difficult to break. The children themselves may resent looking different when they have become used to looking alike.

Parents may fail to appreciate that outfits in similar styles but different colours are often a good compromise. The attraction of the twinship is retained but the children can easily be distinguished at a distance. Consistent colour coding can help to identify MZ twins on an ongoing basis. However, some parents have found that if this becomes too rigid the children may only be comfortable in their given colour, leading to possible problems if or when school uniforms become mandatory.

Different hairstyles can make for ready distinction between the children but the use of personal features, particularly those such as birthmarks or size, can be upsetting for a child. Photography too may reinforce the tendency to treat twins as a unit. Often the children are portrayed together without clearly naming them. In later years the parents of MZ twins will sometimes have difficulty in identifying them from such photos and this can be disconcerting.

continued over

Development continued

Personality and identity

- ■ It is crucial that all concerned with them (whether as family, friends or professionals) think of and treat twins as individuals right from the start

- ■ The development of individuality and identity and its implications for twin children should be discussed in the antenatal period (see **Multiple Pregnancy**) including:

    - choice of names and the advisability of avoiding twin-sounding ones and even the same initials

    - the importance of encouraging grandparents and friends:

        - to avoid giving them identical outfits and gifts as a matter of course
        - to send separate birthday cards

- ■ Staff in hospital and in clinics should always refer to the babies by name and discuss the progress of each separately

- ■ Parents should be encouraged to make the children readily identifiable:

    - from birth with different coloured cot covers, shawls and/or soft toys

    - later with:

        - colours and style of clothes
        - hairstyles
        - toys

- ■ Parents should be informed of different ways to promote the individuality of their children including:

    - spending time alone with each child

    - giving them periods apart from the start

    - encouraging grandparents sometimes to look after just one of the children

    - discouraging friends from always inviting both children

    - providing opportunities for each to develop friendships with other children such as swapping one of another twin pair (perhaps through the local twins club)

continued over

Background

Development continued

Intrapair relationship

From the start, the emotional environment of a twin baby differs from that of a singleton, for he must develop two strong emotional ties simultaneously - with the mother and the co-twin. The age at which twins become distinctly aware of each other appears to vary greatly: some ignore each other for up to eight months while others appear sensitive to each other from the start. However, there is no doubt that the sleeping, feeding and even breathing patterns of one twin baby may be influenced by the other from a very early age[20].

There is no evidence that a strong attachment between twin children reduces the strength of the mother infant relationship. Indeed, it has been shown that twins with a strong attachment to each other during the first two years also relate strongly to their mother[47].

The relationship between twins is unique in being shared by both partners throughout their lives. The intensity of this relationship clearly varies greatly in different pairs. For many the companionship, help, stimulation, comfort and reassurance it offers is of inestimable benefit. For others, the negative aspects such as dependency, conflict and rivalry can become serious handicaps. Some pairs come to over-depend on their twinship and lack confidence on their own, finding it hard to establish an identity except as a part of a twin pair.

The relationship between twins can also give the pair a power and confidence which not only defies parental discipline but can be daunting to other children.

As they grow older, and if space allows, twins often enjoy having a bedroom each that they can make their own. However, initially at least, they may like to continue sharing with each other at night.

Toilet training

Twins tend to toilet train at a later stage than singletons and may at times use their resistance as a means of attracting negative attention. Often, parents assume both children should be trained together but one may well be ready several months before the other. The second twin will often follow his brother's example when he sees the advantages and rewards that go with no longer needing nappies.

Although there should be no pressure for the children to become toilet trained, a problem can arise if entry to a playgroup or nursery is conditional on being clean and dry especially if this divides a pair of twins who are otherwise both ready to start.

continued over

Development continued

Personality and identity continued

■ Different ways of promoting individuality (continued)

   ▪ attending some different sessions at playgroup/nursery (see FF66)

   ▪ participating in different activities (e.g. dancing; sport, painting)

   ▪ encouraging each twin to have individual relationships with adults outside the immediate family (e.g. a godparent or other close friend)

■ Friends and relatives should be encouraged:

   ▪ to distinguish the children by positive features rather than negative (e.g. birthmarks, size)

   ▪ to avoid 'labelling' the children (e.g. the thinner, fatter, good, bad)

Intrapair relationships

■ Parents should be made aware of the identity and dependency problems that can arise in adolescence and adulthood if young twins:

   ▪ are always dressed alike

   ▪ never separated

■ Parents should be encouraged to ensure that each twin has his own territory in which to keep possessions (e.g. shelf, noticeboard, chest)

■ If space allows, parents might also consider

   ▪ giving each twin his own room

   ▪ keeping a second bed or mattress in one or both rooms so that the children can continue to sleep together if they want to

Toilet training

■ When considering toilet training:

   ▪ reassure parents that there is no undue hurry

   ▪ suggest that attention should be focused on one child at a time

■ Health visitors should be aware that twins benefit particularly from attendance at nursery (see FF66) and, if necessary, request that special consideration be given to allow twins to start nursery even if one or both are still in nappies

continued over

Background

Development continued

Behaviour and discipline

Because they have to compete so directly with each other for their mother's time, twins may from an early age adopt strategies designed to attract one to one attention. These can include feeding problems, sleep refusal and antisocial behaviour such as temper tantrums and biting.

Twin children tend to be more easily distracted and to have more difficulty in concentrating. Attention Deficit Hyperactivity Disorder (ADHD) is also more common[39]. Parents may also reinforce the tendency by frequently shifting attention from one child to the other when the twins are together and, when they do spend time on their own with only one, by trying to compensate for their perceived neglect by overstimulation. From infancy onwards a twin child may never spend time alone. This means he has fewer opportunities to experience the solitude which normally gives children the chance to learn about self awareness and to be comfortable alone with themselves.

The combined force of twins can be extremely difficult to manage. Many parents have been disconcerted to find that strategies successfully used in disciplining their older, single born child(ren) are much less effective with twins. MZ preschool boys often pose a particular challenge in this respect.

Such difficulties probably have several origins. A child responds to discipline because he wants the love or respect of the person giving it. If the person with the most influence over him is his twin who, far from restraining him, may actively encourage bad behaviour, he is much less likely to respond to parental pressures. Collusion between the pair can exclude all members of the family, especially if they develop their own secret language. When their combined ingenuity is compounded by also combining physical strength the effects can be quite devastating. Moreover, twins working together in this way may persevere with their mischief-making for longer than would a single born child. Furthermore, in many cases neither will confess to a misdemeanour, making it difficult for parents to allocate blame and punishment appropriately.

A mother of twins may have little chance to give the encouragement and positive reinforcement that she would if she were alone with one child. When interacting with two at the same time much more time has to be spent on keeping order.

There are few better ways of attracting attention than through biting so it is not surprising that this is a common problem in young twins. Often both children are perpetrators and will usually resolve the problem themselves. It may be more difficult if one is always a non-retaliating victim. Although aware that this is not the best way to resolve the situation, many parents may be driven to reinforce the problem by carrying the offender in order to keep him away from his victim.

Development continued

Behaviour and discipline

- Help parents to understand the reasons why they may find disciplining twins more difficult
- Encourage parents to:
    - seek opportunities for praising good behaviour
    - develop a stronger relationship by spending time alone with each child
    - define the few misdemeanours that must be corrected and ignore all others
    - avoid punishments that will affect both children, if only one twin has misbehaved
    - ensure that reprimands and punishments are given to each child individually and in private
- If biting becomes a problem, encourage parents to:
    - ignore it whenever possible
    - avoid giving special attention to the offender, removing him quietly from the scene
    - accompany any necessary action with a firm but quiet reprimand
    - remove the offending child and focus attention on the victim

Background

Family Relationships

The presence of twins can profoundly affect family dynamics and each member may react differently to their arrival.

Mother

For many mothers, relating to <u>one</u> baby is a full-time occupation both emotionally and physically. The complexity of relating simultaneously to twins, in addition to the extra physical effort involved, can often cause enormous strain. Moreover some mothers may initially find it difficult to tell their babies apart and may be further distressed by this confusion, feeling that such an apparent failing in basic maternal instinct must indicate inadequate parenting skills.

At the beginning, every mother of twins will need particular support and understanding, especially if one or both babies are ill and separated from her. It is recognised that mothers find it more difficult to relate to babies from whom they have been separated during the first days following delivery than to those who have been with them throughout[48].

It is much more common for mothers of twins to have to cope with the acute emotional crisis caused by the birth of a premature baby. It has been found that if one of the babies is notably more ill than the other mothers are much more likely to relate to the healthier infant[49]. A mother of twins may find it particularly difficult to handle her confused emotions if one baby is thriving and the other is critically ill.

Size and appearance may also influence the mother's feelings especially in the early days. She may favour the large baby where there is a significant weight discrepancy, feeling that the smaller baby is in some way imperfect[50]. On the other hand, his very smallness and weakness may inspire an urge to provide special care and protection. Several studies have shown this to be the more common reaction, at least during the first year[51-53].

Eye to eye contact is vital to the relationship between mother and infant. If one twin is visually more responsive than the other the mother may unconsciously give that baby more of her attention.

continued over

Family Relationships

Mother

■ In order to facilitate a closer relationship, encourage the mother to:

- make the babies readily distinguishable
- spend time with each baby
- give extra attention to a less responsive baby

■ The mother should be encouraged to recognise differences in the personalities of her babies and to respond accordingly

continued over

Background

Family Relationships continued

Mother continued

Mothers will often notice marked contrasts in the personalities of their babies within a few days of birth and it has been observed that within three weeks most mothers talk and behave differently with each child. These differences are often shown first in individual feeding patterns.

Every mother aims to give her babies the same amount of attention and to love them equally. She often feels guilty if she doesn't and may find it difficult to acknowledge that she prefers one to the other. If one baby is more demanding, the mother may feel both guilty that she is depriving the other twin and resentful that she has to spend so much time on a difficult baby at the expense of one who responds more positively to her attention. Usually this situation will resolve itself after a short time. The more demanding infant often develops into a lively and responsive child to whom the mother can readily relate.

The long-term effects of early mother-twin relationships have yet to be established. On the one hand it has been shown that the influences of these early preferences may be shown in the way that the mother later talks about or responds to each child[54]. On the other hand, a mother may actually make a conscious effort to compensate the less favoured twin by spending more time with him. Almost all parents go through phases of liking one child less than his sibling(s). It is no different with twins. Only if the preference for one becomes entrenched is there likely to be a long-term problem.

At a surprisingly young age, twins may unite against their mother and deliberately ignore her attempts to maintain order. This can be both stressful and upsetting. If a mother always perceives and relates to her twins as a pair rather than as individuals they may in time regard themselves in the same light, becoming even more obdurate. However, the behaviour of even the most disobedient twin child is often transformed when his mother spends even quite short periods of 'quality' time alone with him. Such opportunities enable her to give the child individual praise and encouragement in a way that is rarely possible when the twins are together. This positive experience often leads to lasting improvement in the child's relationship with his mother.

continued over

Family Relationships continued

Mother continued

- Health visitors should be aware of:
  - the guilt and stress that can be caused if one baby is demanding a disproportionate amount of attention
  - the possible need for help with the difficult baby so that the mother does not feel she is neglecting the less demanding twin
- If a mother is experiencing difficulties, reassure her that:
  - it is not unusual for mothers to relate more readily to one baby than the other
  - one baby may need more attention and time spent on him
  - emotional ambivalence is common
  - any feelings of preference usually resolve themselves within a few months
- If the mother consistently shows a preference for one child, the reason for this should be explored
- In cases of oppositional conduct, the mother should be encouraged to:
  - have 'quality' time alone with each child
  - take every opportunity to reinforce and praise good behaviour

continued over

Background

Family Relationships continued

Father

A notable feature of those mothers of twins who cope well during the first years is a good and secure relationship with their partner[1]. The role of the father of twins cannot be overestimated. Neither can his need for adequate support and antenatal preparation. Inevitably, he will be more heavily involved with the babies' care than he would have been of a single born baby and, in general, the earlier he can be encouraged to participate the better. However, even the most supportive father may be apprehensive about handling a small preterm baby. Any trepidation is quite natural but it is important that his confidence should be built up by becoming involved with the care of the babies while they are still in hospital.

Fathers may be deeply affected by the new emotional and financial pressures and may well find difficulty in sharing time and energy between work and home. While the increased living costs may mean working longer hours, there may be feelings of guilt that they are not devoting more hours to helping with the care of the children.

Exhaustion can affect fathers too and may cause friction between the partners. If fathers are regularly woken at night by crying babies it can be very difficult for them to function effectively at work, especially if their jobs involve a high degree of concentration.

Although twins tend to have less contact with either parent than singletons, the proportionate amount of time spent with their father is likely to be greater. It is therefore not surprising that a study found more two-year-old boy twins than singletons choosing their father as the primary figure of attachment[41]. This emphasises the importance of fathers establishing strong one to one relationships with each child.

continued over

Family Relationships continued

Father

During the antenatal period

■ Fathers should be made aware of:

- their crucial role during the early years

- the importance of helping their partner to arrange practical help with the babies and the home well before the twins are born

- the likelihood of sleep deprivation during the early months in order that they may take what preventive measures they can, particularly in relation to working arrangements

■ Fathers should also be given adequate opportunities to ask questions and express their concerns by:

- organising a 'fathers session' (to be led by a healthcare professional and an experienced father of twins) as part of the parent education programme

- encouraging them to make contact with fathers in the local twins club

During the first year

■ Health visitors and family doctors (and, where relevant, social workers) should liaise closely to ensure the provision of appropriate emotional support for fathers, particularly with regard to:

- exhaustion from sleepless nights and the possible effects on:
  - their ability to perform satisfactorily at work
  - their relationship with their partner

- the exceptional stress experienced by many fathers in having to combine unavoidable childcare with their more traditional role as a financial provider

■ Fathers should be encouraged to:

- develop individual relationships with the twins

- make opportunities to spend time alone with each of them

- take one child out while the mother spends time with the other

continued over

Background

Family Relationships continued

Sibling

Parents with an older child or children are always apprehensive about the impact of a new baby on the family and many of the possible problems mentioned below are not exclusive to multiple births. However, they are much more likely to occur where twins or more are concerned.

Even during pregnancy there may be problems. A mother expecting twins may need more intensive antenatal monitoring, requiring frequent hospital visits (see **Multiple Pregnancy**). She may also be admitted as an in-patient, in some cases for long periods. This can create not only practical difficulties with child-care but also cause the older child to resent the new babies before they have even arrived.

If a mother has had a caesarian section (more likely in a multiple pregnancy), she may be less able to cope with the physical demands of caring for and especially carrying a small child. If the mother is discharged before her babies, it may be very hard for her to combine hospital visits with trying to maintain a normal routine for her older child(ren) at home.

Once home, much time will be taken up in caring for the babies. In addition, the new arrivals inevitably attract a great deal of attention with many people tending to focus on them at the expense of the older child.

A single child may feel isolated by the arrival of twins, perceiving both parents and babies as pairs while he has no partner. Later, the older sibling may feel daunted or even excluded by the power of the twin unit once they become toddlers.

Despite their best intentions, it is inevitable that parents will have less time to spend with their older child - in the early days at least. Family outings are more difficult to organise and even taking older children to nursery or school may need careful planning.

The sibling's response to all these factors is likely to be manifested in behavioural changes[55]. The child may either seek attention by behaving badly or in an inappropriately infantile way or by making an enormous effort to win parental approval by being unnaturally good. Sometimes he may just become withdrawn. Many parents have been surprised by such adverse reactions, particularly since the child has often been eagerly awaiting the arrival of two babies, and wish they had given more careful thought to ways of coping with the situation.

continued over

Family Relationships continued

Sibling

For the antenatal preparation of siblings, (see **Multiple Pregnancy**).

In hospital:

- The older child should meet the twins as soon as possible after they are born
- The mother should be encouraged to:
    - first greet the sibling without the twins being present then introduce him to the babies
    - ask grandparents and friends to give special attention to him rather than to the twins
    - think of ways of helping him to relate to each baby individually from the start by:
        - choosing and giving two separate presents which should be prominently displayed in the cots
        - making a card for each
        - giving him a present from each twin

At home:

- The parents should be encouraged to:
    - involve him in the care of the babies without making it obligatory
    - establish a routine activity especially for him (e.g. daily bedtime story)
    - encourage him to develop a rewarding relationship with each of the twin children by:
        - spending time alone at home or going on outings with just one of the twins
        - sleeping with one of the pair rather than assuming that the twins should sleep together
    - seek professional help if there is ongoing concern about their child's behaviour

continued over

Background

Family Relationships continued

Grandparents

Many grandparents greatly enjoy their twin grandchildren, as well as the reflected prestige that twins or more bestow. They develop rewarding and individual relationships with the children and, where they are able to actively support the mother in coping with her extra workload, may get to know their grandchildren better than they might have done with a single child. Grandparents can provide a consistency which all children want but which may be lacking in a multiple birth family.

However, some grandparents (particularly those faced with the arrival of triplets or more) may feel that they are expected to cope with all the children single-handed. The enormity of such a task may overwhelm them and, to avoid it, they distance themselves from the family. Others have found the relationship with multiple birth children less rewarding than with their single born grandchildren. This may be because the children are used to relating to several carers and may therefore not develop such an intimate relationship with their grandparents.

Reliable and consistent help from grandparents can, of course, be invaluable. However such support not infrequently diminishes after the first few months and in other cases the mother becomes frustrated by a lack of predictability in the help provided. Moreover, it is not unknown for proud grandparents to add to the workload in the early days by bringing visitors to see the new babies and expecting the mother to entertain them.

Family Relationships continued

Grandparents

- Encourage grandparents to learn about the implications of a multiple pregnancy and the special issues that may arise in the care and development of the children by:
    - inviting them to attend prenatal talks
    - providing literature
    - introducing them to other grandparents of multiples

- Encourage parents to establish from the start the role the grandparents wish and are able to play in the practical and emotional care of the children by:
    - working out in advance what help that they will need
    - helping the grandparents to:
        - make a realistic appraisal of the type and frequency of support they might be able to give
        - realise that a reliable commitment to provide a little help on a regular basis is much more valuable than vague promises of unlimited support that fail to materialise
    - avoiding dependence on grandparental help unless definite arrangements can be made

- From the start the grandparents should be encouraged to relate to the children as individuals by:
    - always referring to each by name
    - learning to distinguish the children
    - spending time alone with each child
    - giving individual presents, cards etc.
    - avoiding emphasis of the twinship (e.g. by giving non-identical outfits)

- Each child should be helped to develop a special and individual relationship with his grandparents by:
    - visiting them or going out with them separately
    - doing different things with them
    - sending them separate cards and presents

Background

Nursery

Twins and higher order birth children are often not given the high priority for nursery placement that they need if they are to become as well prepared for mainstream school as those that are single born. Twins are likely to have had fewer opportunities for outings and for socialising with other children of their own age and they may not have developed skills such as dressing themselves as well as their peers. Their language skills may also be less advanced and they may have very poor perception of themselves as individuals, especially if they are MZ and always dressed alike – in some cases failing to recognise themselves in photographs or the mirror or even to respond to their own names.

However, because they need more than one place, parents sometimes find it more difficult to get twins accepted even with strong recommendations from social workers and/or health visitors. Only 22 per cent of schools specifically include twins/higher order births in their criteria for admission priority to nursery[56].

Learning patterns are often first acquired in the pre-school period especially if the children are never separated. A less able (or just less confident) twin may establish an entrenched habit of not trying that can be hard to alter later on.

Just knowing that children are twins or triplets (even those that are not 'identical') seems to have the effect of making it very difficult for people to identify them individually or to address them by name. Occasionally, parents themselves seem to take an almost perverse delight in their children being indistinguishable. However, such an inability can have serious repercussions on the development of the child's individuality – as well as the extra difficulties involved in producing accurate progress reports.

School or nursery is often the first opportunity for a child to have experiences that are independent of other members of his family and not necessarily shared with them. Single born children are able to decide for themselves what to tell their parents. Twins do not always have the same opportunity and if one reports all that has happened to the other (whether it be good or bad) the second may find the lack of privacy irritating and even distressing[57]. A triplet may find this even more stressful as the other two may gang up to report any misdemeanour.

Each twin child may welcome the chance at nursery to enjoy experiences unobserved by his brother and to make his own personal friends.

Nursery

■ Twins should be given high priority for admission to nursery

■ Social workers and health visitors should be prepared to support applications for places

■ Consider the advantages for the whole family if each twin attends one session per week on his own, leaving the other child and his mother to enjoy time together at home

■ From the start, parents should be encouraged to make the twins easily distinguishable from each other (e.g. different clothes, shoes or hairstyles)

■ Parents who enjoy the confusion caused by their children looking identical should be informed of:

  the detrimental effect this may have on accurate record keeping and possible long term implications for each child's progress

  the effects on the development of the twins' friendships with other children

  safety issues, particularly in the playground

■ Ensure that all nursery staff:

  are aware of whether the twins have any experience of being separated

  readily recognise each twin and address him by name

  keep accurate records about each child

  encourage both twins to:

  • take part in separate activities

  • speak for themselves

  • acknowledge and accept that they may have different strengths and weaknesses

  look for opportunities to develop the twins' individuality

  fully acknowledge the achievements of each twin

  bolster the self confidence of the twin who finds an activity more difficult

  make allowance for any relatively poor development of such skills as toilet training, dressing and undressing and verbal communication

  implement appropriate intervention as soon as possible to enable the twins to perform at the same level as their single born peers by the time they start mainstream school

■ Parents should be invited to discuss the progress of each child individually and given sufficient time to do this

Background

School

A large study in Australia in 1990 first provided useful data on the then current practices in schools, including the perceptions of parents and teachers in relation to school-age twins[58]. More recently a similar study in the UK confirmed the findings[56].

Although the attitude of individual teachers is the key factor in meeting the needs of multiples, there is still a tendency, in the UK at least, for schools to have rigid attitudes towards their education. Too often, they have a policy of always either keeping the children together in the same class or of separating them, regardless of individual circumstance. Over-dependency, for example, may be a reason for separating twins in one instance and for keeping them together in another.

One form entry schools, of course, have no choice (except where vertical grouping is involved and this can cause further complications) and a significant number of others organise their classes alphabetically or according to age, which means (unsatisfactorily at times) that twins will always be together. However, whatever the circumstances, it is still important to involve parents right from the start and it is disturbing to learn that the UK study found that only one quarter of the 3,000 participating schools liaised with parents over this crucial aspect of their children's school career[56].

Choosing a school

Many twins have no problems when they enter mainstream school and are as happy and successful as single children. A far greater number of twin children will, however, enjoy and benefit fully from their time at school if teachers and parents are made aware of the possible problems and, where necessary, take preventive or remedial action.

Starting school is an important milestone for any child, requiring thought and preparation. When children are twins (and even more so if they are part of a higher multiple set) there are additional aspects to consider. Preterm birth, more common in twins, may have implications for a child starting school. Those whose birth was due in early autumn but who are in fact born before 1 September find themselves facing the challenge of entering school a year earlier than they should have done.

Overall, however, the factor affecting every family is separation: whether the children should be in the same class (or even in the same school) or whether they should start together and separate later. A small minority of parents may envisage keeping their children together throughout their schooling.

continued over

School

■ All schools should:

> adopt a flexible approach to the question of separating twins, assessing each pair individually and taking the whole family into account

> consider using a parent-teacher questionnaire such as the one produced by Tamba and available on its website (see FF106)

Choosing a school

■ In addition to considering available schools on their various merits, parents of twins should be helped (by nursery school teachers, health visitors and/or social workers) to consider:

> the personality and ability of each child

> separation options, i.e. do they want the twins to be:

- in the same class

- different classes

- different schools

- together initially, separating later on

■ When meeting parents for the first time, a head teacher should ascertain if the twins were born preterm and, if so, by how much

■ If the prematurity is significant and it transpires that, say, August born twins should have been born in October, consideration should be given to delaying their start until the following year (or, if the local system allows, at least until the January term)

■ If different schools are chosen, it is important that parents have considered possible difficulties such as:

> introducing the children to school

> transport issues (e.g. taking to and collecting from two schools simultaneously)

> possible clash of events such as Christmas play or parent-teacher evening

> the needs of any other children in the family

continued over

Background

School continued

Choosing a school continued

Factors such as the relative abilities of the individual children are especially important but the final decision may be limited by the way that local schools are structured and by family circumstances (e.g. transport arrangements, other children). Moreover, parents may be more concerned by the reputation of one particular school than by whether or not the children can be in separate classes.

Both Australian and UK studies found that most parents expected their children to be in separate classes by the time they reached secondary school but many felt they had been inadequately consulted about whether or not the children should be separated at an earlier stage. Parental reports on the children's reactions were often not taken into account and the twins themselves were rarely asked for their views.

Contrary to widely held assumption, there was no convincing evidence (in the UK or Australia)[56,58] that separation led to better development of the child's individuality.

Together or apart?

Together

Twins often have less trouble settling into school than single children[44]. Although they are away from their mother, they still have the security that each other provides. If the twins like being together and are not used to being separated, there are definite advantages in starting in the same class. Certainly if they are so dependent on each other that they are miserable when they are apart, separation should not be considered until they have had help to reduce such dependency. This problem usually only arises with twins who have had no previous experience of acting independently.

Although some twins compete excessively (and therefore need to be separated) others benefit from the mutual help, stimulation and mild rivalry that they provide for each other.

It should be noted that sometimes, in an effort to avoid distress to the less able or successful brother, the achievements of a talented twin may not receive due acclaim or recognition (e.g. selection for a team or a prize). For the same reason or because a position cannot be offered to more than one child, twin children are sometimes deprived of opportunities (e.g. to have a part in a play or to be a school prefect). Although such a situation can be hard for both staff and parents to manage, the long term effects of denying an able child the right to function at the level he deserves can include de-motivation and resentment.

continued over

School continued

Together or apart?

Together

- Parents and teachers should consider keeping the twins together (at least in the short term) if the children:
    - have no prior experience of being apart
    - are lacking in self confidence
    - are over dependent on each other
- Steps should be taken to enable the twins to function separately by:
    - always referring to them individually rather than collectively as 'the twins'
    - ensuring that one does not become the spokesman for both
    - putting the twins on different tables
    - putting them in separate reading groups
    - encouraging the twins to make separate friendships
    - trying to give them different tasks
    - helping the parents to devise ways of giving the twins separate experiences:
        - music, sport, dancing etc.
        - suggesting that other parents invite only one twin rather than both
        - allowing the twins to have their own space at home
- If parents would prefer their children to be separated but, for whatever reason, this is not possible, they should be reminded that school is only a part of life and that development of individuality does not only depend on separation there
- Each twin should always:
    - be given access to all the roles available to his peers
    - be selected on his own merit
    - have his achievements appropriately acknowledged
- If he is unduly upset, the other child should be helped to acccept his twin's success and encouraged to develop his own strengths in other areas

continued over

Background

School continued

Apart

One advantage of separating the children is that comparisons and competition are reduced.

Some twins strive to be exactly alike in all their activities. This may mean that the more able child under-achieves while the less able struggles to keep up. In other pairs one may, for example, opt out of a sport or depend on his twin for some areas of homework. It is not uncommon for one child to perceive the other as more competent even when there is no actual difference in their abilities[57].

Parents may become unnecessarily anxious about the children's progress if, being in the same class, their differences are readily seen. Children tend to vary not only in their rates of progress but also in the timing of phases of acceleration and assimilation so that at times the differences between DZ twins may be misleadingly great. (NB Such differences in MZ twins should, however, be a cause for investigation.)

In cases where the twins have clearly differing abilities in one or more areas, they cannot be protected forever from recognising this fact. The earlier they can be helped to accept the differences the easier will they find it and the happier their relationship with each other will become.

Girls tend to develop faster in the early school years and this can be a problem in unlike sex pairs, with the girl often 'mothering' the boy. Initially, he may be quite happy to accept this but in the long-term it may harm his relationship with his peers, particularly other boys.

Although mutual support can be beneficial especially during early days at school, some twins may be too dependent on each other. In the longer term this may affect other relationships, or become so one-sided that the dominant child performs on behalf of both.

Twins together can make a powerful unit that can appear quite threatening to teachers. If they combine forces to be disruptive, they can cause havoc. When they first arrive in school, even well behaved triplets can completely dominate the whole class. In addition to the self-confidence gained from each other, they often have strident voices as a result of constant competition for adult attention. Single born children may be overwhelmed and the teacher may find it hard to create a homogenous group.

Many twins use their 'twinship' to confuse teachers and entertain other children[59]. This is harmless fun in small doses but can become a destructive and attention-seeking habit. They may also distract each other and distractibility has been shown to be a common problem with twins[58].

continued over

School continued

Apart

- Separation should be considered if:

    the parents and/or the twins themselves want it

    the children are:

    - boy-girl pairs

    - indistinguishable (especially if they use this fact constantly to attract attention)

    - of very different ability

    - unduly competitive with each other

    - over dependent on each other

    one is always the spokesman for the pair

    one dominates the relationship (e.g. makes all the decisions)

- Teachers should:

    be aware that the more dominant and apparently more confident child may find separation more difficult than his hitherto dependent twin

    be ready to provide extra support and encouragement in helping the twin(s) to cope alone

    ensure that the twins have reasonable opportunity to see each other during the day, especially during the early days of separation

    liaise with the teacher(s) involved with the other twin to ensure that:

    - they are sensitive to any differences in performance between the twins and the effects these may have at home

    - the children receive similar amounts of homework (if applicable)

    - they are aware when the other child is ill or upset

    - so far as is practicable, the twins maintain similar academic progress

    discuss any emotional or behavioural problems that one or both children may experience

    liaise closely with parents

continued over

Background

School continued

Timing of separation

If twins start school in the same class, the timing of any later separation must be carefully planned. It is usually better if this takes place when a change is anyway due otherwise one will remain in the same room with the same teacher and friends and the other may feel rejected as he sets off alone.

Parent/teacher partnership

Many teachers welcome close collaboration with parents of twins not least because their own experience of them may be limited. Some, however, have developed rigid views on the management of twins after teaching only one or two sets and parents may be disconcerted by their inflexibility.

Despite their best intentions, it is very often difficult for parents and teachers to resist comparing twins with each other rather than with their peers despite knowing that such comparison can both reinforce any differences between them and, in some cases, induce undue competition. Furthermore, this may give a false impression of the children's progress (especially when it is quite similar). On the one hand, the achievements of the second may be under-rated if they are near the top of the class; on the other, slow development in both may not be taken seriously enough if they are at the bottom.

continued over

School continued

Timing of separation

■ Schools should:

> liaise carefully with parents about the timing of any separation

> keep parents fully informed about the reasons for such a decision

■ If the timing means that one child will be remaining with friends and a familiar teacher:

> the children should be fully involved in the decision about which one moves

> parents should be encouraged to report back any reactions at home

Parent/teacher partnership

■ A close parent-teacher partnership is essential so that teachers may be aware of the particular issues affecting individual twins and their families

■ Parents and teachers of twins may need to meet more often than usual

■ A teacher with both twins in the same class should:

> if they are DZ, be discouraged from comparing the two children with each other rather than with their peers

> if they are MZ, investigate if their rates of progress are markedly different

> consider separate appointments for each child when discussing their progress with parents and, if circumstances justify it, another one to discuss the effects of the twin relationship. (If parents can only manage one session, care should be taken to report on each child separately before discussing the twinship)

■ A teacher with only one twin in the class should encourage parents to mention any changes in behaviour at home which may stem from separation at school

■ All teachers should keep parents closely informed about any difficulties at school that may relate to twinship

■ Although twinship may be a contributing factor in a child's poor performance, this should never be a reason for delaying intervention

continued over

Background

School continued

The first term

Teachers usually welcome the arrival of twins and are eager to accept advice from the parents as how best to help the children manage their twinship in school. However, a small minority have fixed ideas about twins, expecting them to be slower than other children, to look identical and to enjoy being treated alike. They assume that the children are indistinguishable and make little effort to tell them apart (even when they are DZ); instead, they see them as a unit with no differences even in personality or abilities. This becomes even more difficult when parents cannot be convinced that there are grave disadvantages to the children when they look exactly the same.

Twins may arrive at school less able than their peers to perform practical tasks such as dressing themselves. If they are in separate classes (and, even more so, if the other twin is in a different school), it can be difficult for a mother to supply the support that each needs to settle happily. The children themselves may become very distressed if they are denied opportunities to meet regularly during the day.

In the past, twins' language skills tended to be less advanced when they started school and this affected their ability to contribute in class and to make progress with reading and writing skills. However, it appears that greater awareness of these problems may now be preventing these disadvantages. A recent study showed no significant difference in communication skills between twins and single born children at primary school[40]. Few teachers receive specific training on the special needs that twins, particularly boy twins, may have such as reading difficulties and distractibility.

It is inevitable that when twins are in separate classes comparisons are made between those who teach them, especially if parents feel that one teacher is notably better than the other. There can also be problems, especially in primary school, if the work programme follows a different order. For example, one child may be labelled a failure at home if he is not perceived to be making the same progress as his twin (e.g. a slightly less advanced reading book)[57].

The UK study found that more than 50 per cent of twins were themselves upset if the other was ill or upset[56]. When the children are in separate classes teachers may underestimate the extent to which what is happening to one child may affect the other.

continued over

School continued

The first term

- When twins (or higher multiples) first arrive at school, teachers should:
  - encourage the parent to bring to school for the first week or two another adult who is well known to the children so that each child can have someone to help him settle in
  - be prepared for the possibility that twins may overwhelm the other children in the class

- Teachers should be encouraged to:
  - think of the children as individuals
  - call them by name and to avoid referring to them as 'the twins'
  - reward individual achievement on its merits and not refrain from doing so because it might upset the other twin who has not attained the same level
  - suggest that the twins are clearly identifiable by features such as hairstyles, shoes, clothing

- When messages are to be carried by children to and from school, the teacher should either:
  - give each child his own message (even if the twins are in the same class) or
  - ensure that the twins take it in turn to be the messenger

continued over

Background

School continued

Friends

Many twin children are popular and make friends easily. They are used to cooperative games and often find these easier than individual activities. On the other hand, some may find outside relationships daunting. This particularly applies to those who have enjoyed little or no opportunity to relate on their own to other children and have relied exclusively on each other for companionship. Such circumstances may mean that they do not have the opportunity to develop the social skills necessary for developing friendships. When faced with a large group of children they may become even more isolated and dependent upon each other. One study found that one fifth of five-year-old twins stuck together and had few outside friends[56]. In the same study, 44 per cent shared the same friends and less than 10 per cent had mainly separate friends.

MZ twins, particularly girls, always cause interest and, through this, may attract friends without needing to make the social effort otherwise required to develop friendships. As a result, they may find it quite difficult when they are separated and are no longer recognised as part of an interesting pair.

Twins and triplets often find that they receive fewer invitations than singletons. Other parents sometimes assume that the children must always be together so, daunted by the prospect of coping with the pair or trio in addition to their own child(ren), they decide not to invite them.

School continued

Friends

■ Parents should be encouraged to help their children develop their own relationships and friendships with other children from an early age by:

- sending each child to nursery on his own (e.g. separately for two days and together for one)

- encouraging other parents, friends and family to invite one child at a time (e.g. birthday parties)

- arranging regular 'half swaps' with another family with similar aged twins

- inviting another child to spend time with one of the twins whilst the other is cared for by someone else

- allowing a consistent relationship to develop, where possible, between one twin and a particular friend

- encouraging relatives to invite one child at a time

Background

Illness and Disability

Acute illness

If they are born preterm, twins (like any premature baby) will be vulnerable to infection during the early months. Apart from this, twins are in general no more prone to most physical illnesses than single born children. However if one child has an infectious illness, it is much more likely that his twin will contract it too. Caring for sick twins may be not only emotionally draining but also practically hazardous in terms of confusion over medication and the administration of some therapies such as steam inhalation. Visiting the doctor's surgery with ill twins poses a logistical nightmare. Neither can be given the attention they need and/or demand and it is impossible to carry two toddlers at the same time.

If one twin has to go into hospital during the early years, the effect on both children may be profound, particularly if they have never previously been apart and/or the admission is unexpected. Unlike single born children, one of the twins in such a situation will be faced with the trauma of separating simultaneously from his brother and from his mother. Regrettably, but not surprisingly, many hospitals will not allow admission to the healthy twin. If both infants are still being breastfed, the mother may feel under additional strain because of the logistical problems of maintaining the routine.

Accidents

No figures are available on the accident rate in twins but it would be surprising if it were not relatively high. It is more difficult to keep an eye on two active toddlers simultaneously. Furthermore, the combination of mutual encouragement and physical cooperation is likely to lead not only to much more reckless activity but the accomplishment of feats at an earlier age than a child on his own would achieve. Parents develop a remarkable ability to keep an eye on several children at the same time; other relatives and carers usually find this difficult. An added danger can arise for MZ twins if they are dressed alike. At a distance they may be indistinguishable and parents, teachers and other carers may not be able to shout a personal warning in an emergency.

Serious injury can lead to long term disability and/or disfigurement. For the affected twin, especially MZ, the constant reminder of what his appearance and abilities should be may increasingly induce frustration as he grows older. Meanwhile, his brother may feel guilty that he is growing up unscathed. For the same reason, if the father or mother was directly responsible for such an accident, the contrast between the children exacerbates feelings of remorse and grief and may adversely affect the parents' relationship with each other.

continued over

Illness and Disability

Acute illness

■ Parents of young twins, whether one or both are ill, should be advised that:

   they should keep particularly careful records of medication

   some therapies such as steam inhalation can be more dangerous

   strenuous efforts to prevent the second twin contracting an illness are probably pointless

■ All surgery staff should be made aware of the extra difficulties encountered by one parent bringing ill twins to the doctor

■ When twins are ill, one of the following may well be needed:

   an appointment outside normal surgery hours

   assistance with the children in the waiting and consulting rooms

   a home visit (even if this would not normally be justified)

■ Every effort should be made in cases of hospital admission to ensure that both twins can maintain close and prolonged contact with their mother and each other especially if:

   they have never previously been separated

   they are still being breastfed

   it is the parents' wish

■ If the healthy twin is not admitted, and is old enough to understand what is happening, he should be told:

   where his twin is (and, if possible, shown the place)

   what is happening to his twin

   when he is going to see him again

Accidents

■ Health visitors should emphasise to parents the importance of:

   creating as safe an environment as possible once the children are mobile (one twin/triplet-proof area is the answer for some families)

continued over

Background

Chronic illness and disability

Having a chronically ill or disabled child is always very hard for parents. Where twins are involved, the emotional and practical upheaval may be even greater especially if the children are MZ, with the possible genetic consequences involved. The way the diagnosis is given can have long term effects, particularly on parent-professional relationships - as can sensitive acknowledgement of the additional problems facing a multiple birth family in such circumstances (see **Special Needs in Twins and more**).

In some cases, of course, the diagnosis will be made at birth – or even antenatally. However, in others parents may become anxious about their child's physical or mental development and it is not uncommon for them to be told by healthcare professionals that any delay is 'just because they're twins'. Although DZ twins often have very different rates of development and parents are often unduly alarmed by any discrepancy, blanket dismissal of their concerns on the grounds of twinship is not helpful – and may even be erroneous. Any disparity between MZ twins, particularly if this is increasing, is always a cause for investigation.

The disabilities experienced by multiple birth children are of course the same as those suffered by singletons. However, the origin of the impairment may be unique to twins (e.g. the twin-twin transfusion syndrome; the effect of an intrauterine death on the surviving twin) or occur with greater frequency (e.g. cerebral palsy or intellectual impairment). Furthermore, the implications of having a twin child with special needs can be more complex than with a single child and the very special needs of the unaffected child are often inadequately recognized. (For more information see **Special Needs in Twins and more**).

Many forms of disability are more common in twins, mainly due to long term complications of a preterm birth. In the few population based studies the incidence of cerebral palsy has been found to be significantly increased in multiples. One study found that the chance of a child having cerebral palsy was 0.2 per cent for singletons, 1.3 per cent for twins and 7.6 per cent for triplets - a relative risk of 1:6.5:38[60]. Following the death of a co-twin or triplet before birth the risk is still greater[60].

There is little information on the frequency of learning difficulties in twins. Even if they start more slowly, many catch up with their singleton peers by the time they reach school[61]. However, a large study in Australia found that although girl twins achieved as well as singletons in numeracy and literacy skills by 13 years, many boy twins continued to have difficulties beyond that age[62].

continued over

Illness and Disability continued

Accidents continued

■ Health visitors should emphasise to parents the importance of:

ensuring that one child is safe before they attend to the other

ensuring that, when they are out, they or other carers either have a hand for each child or some other form of restraint (e.g. a harness)

being easily able to distinguish between the children (from behind as well as the front) when out so that they can call out a warning by name

Chronic illness and disability

■ Ensure that parental concerns about the development of their twin(s) are investigated, especially MZ pairs

■ When a diagnosis of chronic illness or disability is made:

impart the news sensitively, fully explaining the short and long-term implications:

- for the affected twin
- for his brother

provide information about relevant support groups

■ Encourage parents to pay special attention to the needs of the unaffected child

■ Ensure that they receive adequate practical support in attending specialist appointments

■ Parents should be reminded of the importance of allowing each child to develop as an individual by:

not over-emphasising the twinship (by dress or by calling them 'the twins')

providing appropriate and therefore often separate activities

being careful not to let the twinship affect the management of either child

having time alone with each child by:

- finding someone prepared to be trained in the care of the disabled child
- arranging for each child to be cared for by someone outside the immediate family on a regular basis

continued over

Background

Illness and Disability continued

Because most parents are proud of having twins they may find it hard to stop treating them in exactly the same way, even if one has severe difficulties. This artificial imposition of 'twinness' can become an added burden for one or both children. Indeed, by trying to always keep the children together, the development of the more advanced child may be held back.

The twin with special needs

The child with a disability will find it difficult to understand why, in some respects at least, he does not have the same abilities as his twin. Many are keen to understand their disability and an explanation may bring relief and, if the cause of their impairment was severe neonatal illness, even a feeling of triumph that they have survived.

Although appropriate praise for achievement is usually appreciated, the disabled twin may resent exaggerated praise even more than a single born child because he is able to measure his own performance against his twin's and see clearly the difference that exists. Similarly, he may suffer if he and his twin are not exposed to similar boundaries and discipline from parents and teachers whenever possible.

It is inevitably painful for the disabled child to watch his co-twin doing things he may never be able to do and MZ twins are faced with the constant image of how they might have been. Later, a child may resent the fact that his brother is able to become increasingly independent while he cannot. Jealousy, anger and sometimes depression are not uncommon.

There are, however, positive aspects of being a twin rather than a single born child with special needs. His unaffected brother is a constant source of stimulation, with friends who are able to provide opportunities to mix with and relate to many more healthy children of his own age than might otherwise be the case.

The child with a disability may well benefit from opportunities to be independent of his family - including his twin – so that he can make progress at his own speed and form his own relationships.

continued over

Illness and Disability continued

The twin with special needs

■ Parents should be helped to prepare the phases of explanation according to the child's level of understanding, including:

> the nature of the disability and how it affects the child

> the cause of the disability

> the reason that his brother can do things that he himself cannot

> books with relevant stories about disability, twins and preterm or ill babies

■ Parents should also be encouraged to:

> provide, wherever possible, the same clear guidance and discipline for both twins

> acknowledge all achievements but avoid overcompensating with inappropriate praise

■ Parents and the child should be offered counselling where indicated or requested

■ During adolescence parents should beware of always attributing unusual behaviour to the child's disability particularly when this may be simply a manifestation of puberty

■ Parents should be helped to find respite or other care for their disabled child so that they can devote time to the unaffected twin

continued over

Background

Illness and Disability continued

The unaffected twin

It is not unusual for the sibling of a child with a disability to present with signs of psychological stress. When the sibling is a twin there are likely to be additional, specifically twin related difficulties.

As the differences in behaviour and development become apparent, the unaffected twin may become distressed by the fact that his twin is behaving and being treated differently and that his own achievements are overshadowed by his brother's smaller accomplishments.

The care of the unaffected child tends often to be delegated to friends and relations from an early age and he may soon grow to resent his mother's apparent favouritism towards his twin. The constant friendly attention of the many healthcare workers towards his brother may add to his feelings of rejection. This may lead to attention seeking behaviour which may even include welcoming or exaggerating illness or contriving accidents. His behaviour may regress as he imitates his twin.

Furthermore his own activities and social life may be curtailed by the limitations of his twin, restricting some family outings. In addition, he may feel embarrassed or reluctant to invite friends to the house. Later, complex emotions including jealousy, guilt and a burden of responsibility are not uncommon and he may spend an undue amount of time caring for his brother, often at the expense of his own activities.

Illness and Disability continued

The unaffected twin

■ Parents should be encouraged to:

help the child from an early age to understand the difficulties faced by his brother, the reasons for them and the implications for the family

reassure the child that he is not going to be similarly affected nor is he in any way responsible for his brother's problems

■ The possible reactions and feelings of the child at different ages should be discussed with the parents and they should be helped to prepare for his questions

■ Friends and relatives should be asked to avoid always focusing attention on the twin with a disability

Background

Child Abuse

There is little accurate data on child abuse in twins but it appears to be significantly higher in these families[63] and the singleton siblings may be at as great a risk as the twin children[64]. In general, it is more common for only one of the pair to be abused and when this is the case the affected child tends to be disadvantaged in some way, usually by disability or neonatal complications. A disparity in development or responsiveness has been shown to be a key factor in these cases[63]. When both children are abused it is more likely that the mother is suffering from severe psychosocial problems[63].

If one child only has been abused and it is considered necessary to remove him from his family a dilemma arises as to whether he should be separated from his twin or whether both children should be placed in care. There is no easy answer but whatever happens the children should be allowed to keep in touch with each other.

Parental preference for one twin is not uncommon and when favouritism changes from one to the other over a period of days or weeks it is not a cause for concern. However, if one child is consistently and obviously favoured, his twin may become emotionally damaged. Moreover, in its more serious forms, such neglect can lead to growth retardation or developmental delay in the affected child.

Child Abuse

- Professional carers should be aware of the risk of child abuse (both physical and emotional) if parents consistently favour one twin

- Suspected abuse of a twin should of course be managed according to established guidelines for single born children

- Additional factors for the other twin that should be considered include:

    the risk that he will be abused too

    the psychological effects of witnessing the abuse of his twin

- If it is necessary to remove the abused child from the family, consideration should be given to:

    the emotional effects on both twins of separation from each other

    ensuring that the new carers have an insight into and respect for the importance of the twin relationship

    maintaining contact between the twins

    whether it would be better to remove both twins in order that they can be kept together

Background

Death - The Single Surviving Twin[M]

A twin has a greater risk of death from conception right through the first ten years of life[65]. Thus many more parents of twins and twin children are likely to experience bereavement than those with single born children. In this section we shall concentrate on the surviving child. The bereavement of the parents is discussed fully in **Bereavement**.

Usually only one of the twins will die. The number of single surviving twin children in the UK is difficult to determine, especially if early pregnancy loss is included, but numbers of twin children whose twin was stillborn or died in childhood is estimated as between 5 and 15 per cent of all twin pairs[66].

The death of a twin child has in many respects the same effect on the members of his family as that of a single born child, but there are some aspects of the bereavement that are different. The surviving twin will never have known life without a (mostly constant) partner of the same age.

Perinatal death

The perinatal mortality (stillbirths and deaths in the first week) is five times higher in twins and 10 times in triplets[67]. The main contributor to this high death rate is prematurity and its complications (see **Multiple Pregnancy**). Parents who lose one twin face particular problems and their loss is often underestimated (See **Bereavement**)[68].

Furthermore the parents often feel a double bereavement. They lose not only a precious child but also their special status as parents of twins.

The surviving twin may suffer not only from his own sense of loss but also from the effects of being brought up by grieving parents who may idolise the child who has died. A number of adult survivors have felt that their parents either blamed them for the intrauterine death of their twin or that they would have preferred the other child to have survived instead, particularly where it was of the opposite sex[69].

The child may be bewildered by the fact that special events such as birthdays and starting school, which are happy occasions for most families, make his parents sad.

continued over

Death - The Single Surviving Twin^M

Perinatal death

Many of the needs of the surviving twin and of his parents will be shared by all bereaved siblings and parents. Here we focus on the particular issues raised by the loss of a twin, triplet and more.

- All single surviving twins, as well as their parents, should be offered counselling as required. As part of this it is essential that the uniqueness of twinship should be both acknowledged and given appropriate respect

- Parents should be encouraged to create memories of the dead baby by:

  naming the baby

  taking photographs of the baby both alone and with the twin. A photograph of the two babies together should be taken whenever possible. Otherwise two photographs can be merged or an artist can prepare an attractive sketch using the original photographs. This can also be helpful if the dead baby is disfigured

- As long as there are no medical contraindications, the babies should spend some time together so that the survivor can later be told of this closeness. A video recording and photographs should be considered

- Where the child is not aware of being a twin, parents should be helped to consider how they are going to break the news. Although, in general, the earlier this is done the easier it is likely to be, parents should nonetheless be reassured that a further short delay is often wise in order that:

  they are themselves emotionally prepared for the child's possible reactions (e.g. sadness, guilt, anger, pride, indifference)

  the child understands, perhaps through bedtime stories, the concept of:

  - twins (or higher multiple births)
  - prematurity and low birthweight and that small or preterm babies sometimes die

  teachers and close friends know that he is to be told so that they are prepared for his comments and questions

continued over

Background

Death - The Single Surviving Twin

Perinatal death continued

The child whose twin has died in the perinatal period may later feel distress, anxiety or even just curiosity. Some, however, may not express these feelings for fear of upsetting their parents. On the other hand they may have complex reactions to the death. Many feel angry: angry with the twin for deserting them; for causing such unhappiness in the family; for making them as the survivor feel guilty. They may also feel anger towards their parents for 'allowing' the twin to die. Others feel guilty that they have survived, particularly if at the expense of their twin (as, for example, in the twin-twin transfusion syndrome).

Many surviving twins feel relief when they finally talk about their twin, sometimes not until many years later. In the past many surviving twins of a perinatal death did not discover that they were a twin until adulthood. Most professionals would now agree that both parents and children are likely to cope better with their bereavement if the dead baby is freely talked about from the start. The surviving child often treasures mementoes of his brother or sister. These can include photographs showing the two babies spending time together. Naming the stillborn baby makes it easier for the child to refer to his twin in later life.

Those parents who delay telling the survivor often find it increasingly difficult to break the news. They also risk the child discovering the truth from other sources and being puzzled that such an important part of his life should have been hidden from him. The reactions of those children who are only told that they are one of twins later in childhood vary from indifference, distress or confusion to elation, pride and curiosity. Some who did not discover until adulthood have said that the revelation explained a long-held inner feeling of loneliness.

Too often, when a twin child dies early in life, he is never mentioned. Teachers and even nursery staff may not know of the twin and therefore miss the chance of giving comfort and explanation to a bereaved child.

Sudden Infant Death Syndrome

The incidence of Sudden Infant Death Syndrome (SIDS) in twins appears to be about twice that of infants in general[70] but this increase is confined to low birthweight twins[71]. If one twin dies the second is also at increased risk for up to one month, with the first few days being the most crucial[72]. Many paediatricians would recommend admitting the baby to hospital for observation for a few days.

continued over

Death - The Single Surviving Twin
continued

Perinatal death continued

- After the child has been told, parents might be encouraged to:

  - offer to show him places associated with his twin such as the hospital where they were born and the baby's grave

  - consider introducing him to an adult or older child whose own twin has died in infancy

  - be prepared for his interest and emotions to vary from time to time

Sudden Infant Death Syndrome

- The management of parental bereavement is well covered by literature provided by the Foundation for the Study of Infant Death and other sources. When the child who dies is a twin, additional factors need to be considered

- The surviving baby should be:

  - seen and examined immediately by a doctor

  - closely monitored for at least the next week (unless 24 hour medical surveillance is available at home, admission to hospital is usually recommended)

continued over

Background

Death - The Single Surviving Twin
continued

Death in childhood

Before death

When a twin dies in childhood, whether from accident, chronic illness or acute infection, the effects on the survivor can be devastating. These are likely to be greater where the twins have had little experience of being separated or where the one who died was the 'leader'.

A twin can only be prepared for life without his constant partner if he is as closely involved with his brother or sister's illness and death as his level of understanding allows. He may have fears, unspoken or acknowledged, that he may catch the same illness or indeed die. The dying child may have outstanding business to settle before he dies, such as deciding to whom his special possessions should go.

continued over

Death - The Single Surviving Twin

Death in childhood

Before death

■ In cases where one twin has a terminal illness all staff concerned with the family should be aware of the particular difficulties that may be faced by the other twin

■ Parents should be offered advice and counselling to help them to:

- cope with the emotional stress of relating to a child who may provide a constant reminder of their ill or dead child

- consider how and when to tell the other child that his twin is going to die

- tell the child:
  - how the illness is likely to progress
  - what form the death is likely to take

- be prepared for any questions or worries the child may have

- reassure the child:
  - that (when it is the case) he will not die of a similar illness
  - that he is in no way responsible for his brother's death
  - of his value as an individual son and child

■ Parents should be encouraged to:

- allow the child to spend time with his twin and to be involved with his care according to his age and inclination

- provide another adult who is fully informed of the situation and available to talk to the child when they, themselves, are otherwise occupied or unduly distressed

- keep in close touch with nursery and school staff so that they can provide appropriate support to the child

continued over

Background

Death - The Single Surviving Twin

Death in childhood continued

After death

It can be reassuring for a surviving twin to see his dead brother and to find how peaceful he looks. Parents will decide how much he will be involved in the preparation of the coffin and whether he will attend the funeral. However, even quite a young child may have his own clear wishes and these should be taken into account.

A surviving child may resent the premature sorting or discarding of his dead twin's belongings by parents and teachers, often without consultation. For many children this process can be a necessary part of coming to terms with the death and it usually needs to be done gradually.

A surviving twin may well feel guilty, after the death, that he was the one chosen to live. This guilt, of course, is compounded if he comes to think that he was directly or indirectly responsible for his twin's death and even more so if the parents seemed to have preferred the other child. He will feel even more inadequate if his parents have placed undue store on being 'parents of twins' and too often betray this aspect of their grief.

Many parents, while still grieving themselves, find the survivor's disturbed behaviour extremely stressful. This is often reinforced in MZ twins by the constant reminder of the dead child provided by the survivor - not only in appearance but also in behaviour.

Some surviving twins find it extremely hard to come to terms with becoming the sole focus of their parents' (and others') attention. This is particularly likely when death follows a long illness during which the 'healthy' twin may inevitably have felt neglected.

Death - The Single Surviving Twin
continued

Death in childhood continued

After death

■ Parents should be encouraged to:

consider whether the child:

- should see his twin after death

- would like to be involved with the preparation of the coffin, possibly adding some toy, picture or other object of his own

- should go to the funeral and if so whether they would like another adult to accompany him

- would like to help create and care for the grave by, for instance, planting some bulbs

- should be introduced to an adult whose twin died in childhood. Contacts are available through the Lone Twin Network (see FF106)

seek professional help if:

- they are concerned by the behaviour of their child

- they or their child would like counselling support at any time, possibly many years after the twin's death

Background

Adoption

When considering placement of a twin for adoption there is an additional critical factor to be considered, that of the twinship itself[73]. In the past, twins who were being adopted were often separated. A study has shown that twins who have been adopted separately in infancy often go later to extreme lengths to trace their twin sibling[74]. Many of these twins who subsequently find each other develop a deep and lasting relationship and commonly bitterly resent the fact that they were deprived of this uniquely close relationship through their formative years. Although these feelings are not limited to like sex twins or to one gender, it has been suggested that the intensity is probably greater amongst female pairs of twins or in the female of an unlike sex pair. Those separated in infancy may grieve for their twin for the rest of their lives in a way very similar to many single surviving twins whose twin has died at or soon after birth. This intensity of feeling is not limited to MZ or even to like sex twins but is rarely seen with non-twin siblings.

Most adoption agencies would now agree that healthy twins should be placed together. There is more disagreement about such a policy for twins where one is ill or has special needs. Inevitably in such cases the choice of placements will be reduced and the adoption of the healthy child may therefore be delayed. Furthermore some would question whether the healthy child should have the possible burden of a disabled twin sibling when this could be avoided by separate placement.

A dilemma also arises if only one of the children is placed in care either because the biological parents wish to keep one of twins or if one of the pair has been abused.

If one twin only is placed for adoption, he may have the added burden of feeling that a twin sibling had been chosen by his parent(s) in deliberate preference to himself. Not only would such a child be deprived of his twin but he would inevitably feel an even greater degree of rejection than if both had been placed for adoption because the parent was thought incapable of caring for any child at all.

Adoption

- When the twins are to be adopted together, ensure that potential adoptive parents have:

    knowledge about twins in general

    realistic guidance as to the emotional and physical demands of two babies

    clarified their own motives for adopting two babies/children

    an introduction to the local twins club

    relevant literature on twins

- When only one of a pair of twins is to be adopted, ensure that:

    adoptive parents have knowledge about twins in general and an insight into and respect for the possible importance that the twinship may have for their adopted child

    the children are given the opportunity to maintain their relationship as twins with dependable ongoing contact with each other

    the frequency and length of contact is sufficient to allow the children to maintain a close relationship that will enable them to develop a mutually pleasurable and emotionally supportive relationship later in life if they so wish

Background

Triplets and Higher Order Births

Parenting triplets or more presents particular difficulties and, although most of the basic advice given to parents of twins still applies, very specific additional support is needed, especially in areas of feeding and transportation. The costs involved in providing for three extra babies are very high[75] and financial pressures can be greatly increased by discovering that both home and car are too small to cater for the additional members of the family.

Approximately two third of triplets are born as a result of some form of treatment for infertility, with routine scans being carried out within the first eight weeks. A diagnosis is therefore often made early in the pregnancy. Reactions of mothers expecting triplets or quads range from feelings of bewilderment, panic and loneliness to euphoria. These emotions may be affected by the way the diagnosis is given (see **Multiple Pregnancy**).

The mother may well be admitted to hospital during the pregnancy and even if she is not the babies are likely to be delivered preterm (the average gestation for triplets is about 34 weeks). Worries about not being organised at home will only add to an already stressful situation.

Knowledge of the increased risks to the pregnancy may mean that parents and indeed some professionals are reluctant to prepare for the future in case some or all of the babies do not survive. Local government departments such as Social Services and Housing vary greatly in their response to the needs of higher order birth families. The best provide a wide range of support including help with night care but even they sometimes refuse to make arrangements for practical help, childcare and larger accommodation until all the babies are ready to come home. Consequently, it is not unusual for triplets to have their hospital stay unnecessarily prolonged because of delay in implementing essential support mechanisms. This, in turn, imposes additional strain and cost on overstretched neonatal units. In other areas, departments will not even consider helping triplet families unless there are issues of child protection. Such arbitrary 'postcode' allocation is, in the poorly resourced areas, unfair for the families and frustrating for their professional carers.

continued over

Triplets and Higher Order Births

The needs of families with higher order birth children are mostly similar to, but greater than those with twins. Here we highlight aspects of particular importance. The care of the mother during the pregnancy is covered in more detail in **Multiple Pregnancy**.

- As soon as the diagnosis of a higher order pregnancy is made:

  - provide the parents with:

    - a contact name and telephone number of a mother of triplets, or of a support group involving higher order births

    - an early appointment to discuss the management and implications of the pregnancy

- Family doctors and health visitors must be aware of:

  - the particular medical, practical and emotional problems that can arise for the mother and the rest of the family

  - current sources of information and help

  - the need for a home visit assessment not later than the second trimester

- It is essential that provision for supporting the parents both before and after the birth of the babies be made well in advance especially if there are older children

- During the pregnancy:

  - involve the father in all discussions from an early stage

  - discuss the amount and type of help that will be required and how this may be acquired (e.g. home help, nursery nurse, Home Start volunteers)

  - involve the Social Services in planning (unless the parents have the means to pay for all the help they will require)

  - where appropriate and with the parents' agreement, involve Social Services in relation to:

    - any support needed during pregnancy (e.g. childcare, transport)

    - housing

    - help with childcare and housework after the babies are born

continued over

Background

Triplets and Higher Order Births
continued

After the babies come home, it is almost impossible for parents of triplets to cope without some additional help, especially in the early months when the babies are likely to require frequent feeding day and night. Even if parents can afford to pay, deciding what help will be most useful can be daunting for somebody with little or no experience of caring for small children or of employing people. Parents can even find it difficult to handle offers of help from friends and relatives. This may involve drawing up rotas and assigning specific tasks (the latter may be especially hard) as well as coping with an army of helpers coming in and out.

It should also be remembered that although other members of the family may, in advance, promise to provide help this does not always materialise. As the Triplet Study revealed, grandparents in particular may find themselves overwhelmed by the situation and are therefore much less useful than the parents had hoped[7] (see FF64).

Triplet parents are also likely to receive many visitors, often uninvited, who come to admire the babies but who not only do nothing to help but even expect both attention and cups of tea. This can cause a surprising degree of extra strain, particularly if a mother is already sensitive about her abilities to cope in her new role.

However, after this early attention, isolation can become a particular problem for a mother of triplets. The practical tasks involved with caring for the babies at home leaves little or no time and energy for outings. It may require more planning and effort than an exhausted mother can muster to get the babies out of the house. Furthermore, triple buggies are unwieldy and too large for many doorways. In blocks of flats a narrow lift can pose an insurmountable obstacle.

A further disincentive to going out is the amount of attention that the babies attract. Even walking down the road often results in a seemingly constant stream of uninvited comments and questions from complete strangers. These can become intensely irritating and offensively intrusive.

continued over

Triplets and Higher Order Births
continued

■ During the pregnancy:

  encourage the parents:

  - not to rely on relatives and friends unless they are able to give a firm commitment to regular help
  - to discuss with other parents of triplets:
    - how to establish a regular routine
    - how best to organise the house to simplify all activities before investing in expensive equipment
    - how to handle or avoid interest from the media
    - how to respond to intrusive strangers

■ When the babies come home the family will need:

  regular visits from the health visitor

  home rather than clinic visits for weighing and immunisation

  separate sessions with each baby for medical checks and immunisation

  help at night during the early months in many cases

■ The family should be allocated a named lead professional (e.g. GP, health visitor, social worker) through whom all concerns and enquiries should be channelled

continued over

Background

Triplets and Higher Order Births

Visits to clinics and doctors' surgeries may cause difficulty not least because prams and buggies are rarely allowed inside. It is not unreasonable to ask a mother of a single born child to carry her baby into the waiting area or consulting room. Where triplets are concerned such a feat becomes a physical impossibility.

It is even less appropriate for triplets to be given a single shared appointment than twins, not only for the sake of the children but also to avoid confusion for the health care professionals, particularly where procedures are involved. Cases of inadvertent repeat immunisation of one baby are not unknown.

Information on the longterm development of triplets is still sparse. However, it would appear that the majority do well but the overall incidence of disability is even higher than in twins, due to the long term effects of extreme prematurity and low birthweight.

Triplets experience many of the same pleasures and problems as twins but there are also differences[76]. In general they may be less dependent on each other than a twosome. On the other hand the dynamics of a threesome can sometimes be difficult, particularly if two of the children 'pair'. This may be due to gender, simply to an innate affinity or to zygosity (where an MZ pair can form a threatening unit to a DZ triplet of the same sex).

However, triplet dynamics do not necessarily remain constant. Conflict may arise within a usually inseparable pair, each of whom may then seek the friendship of the 'odd one out'.

Many parents, particularly those who have had many years to plan parenthood, become frustrated by their inability to give each child the individual attention that they deserve. The constant competition, fighting and noise can become wearing for the most tolerant. Even those parents with material resources and plenty of help, may suffer emotional stress, sometimes requiring psychiatric treatment[77].

Occasionally, one child clearly resents the fact that he is part of a trio and, to demonstrate this, may display aggression towards his siblings or other attention-seeking behaviour. This situation may be temporary and resolve itself. At other times, however, it may be an ongoing problem.

Triplets and Higher Order Births
continued

- To stimulate the children's development parents should be encouraged to provide each child with regular opportunities for:

  - periods of peaceful joint activities

  - time alone with an adult

  - relating on their own to another child

- If two of the children tend to exclude the third, parents should be encouraged to:

  - regularly divide the pair so that each can spend time on his own with the third

  - reduce the attention given by others to a MZ pair by dressing them differently

  - arrange for a fourth child to join in the family activities

  - consider dividing the pair at nursery

- If one child becomes isolated or withdrawn, encourage extra time alone with their mother or father

- The lead professional should continue to give parents the opportunity to discuss any concerns and stress they may be experiencing with the children or in their own relationship

- All professionals should bear in mind that praise and encouragement are especially appreciated by parents of triplets and higher multiples

- When a child appears to resent being a triplet:

  - help the parents to alleviate the situation by:

    - allowing the child to express his frustration

    - reassuring him that later on he will be able to be wholly independent of his brothers

    - helping him to enjoy the advantages of having two constant companions in the meantime

  - encourage the parents to avoid emphasising the tripletship

Useful Addresses

Organisations specifically concerned with multiple births

The Multiple Births Foundation (MBF)
(including twins clinics, telephone advisory service, professional education, resource centre)

Hammersmith House - Level 4
Queen Charlotte's and Chelsea Hospital
Du Cane Road
London W12 0HS

Tel: 020 8383 3519
Fax: 020 8383 3041

e-mail: mbf@ic.ac.uk

Website: www.multiplebirths.org.uk

Twins and Multiple Births Association (Tamba)
(including support groups for supertwins, bereavement, special needs, one parent families, adoption, infertility and adult multiples)

Harnott House
309 Chester Road
Little Sutton
Ellesmere Port CH66 1QQ

Tel: 0151 348 0020 (times: 9am - 2pm weekdays)

e-mail: enquiries@tambahq.org.uk

Website: www.tamba.org.uk

Tamba Twinline
(listening and information service run by parents of multiples)

Tel: 01732 868000
(times: 7pm - 11pm weekdays and 10am - 11pm weekends)

Lone Twin Network (LTN)
(for adult twins whose twins have died)

PO Box 5653
Birmingham B29 7JY

Useful Addresses

International Society for Twin Studies (ISTS)
(including Twin Research)

Queensland Institute of Medical Research
Royal Brisbane Hospital
300 Herston Road
Brisbane 4029
Australia

Tel: +61 7 3362 0278
Fax: +61 7 3362 0101

e-mail: ists@qimr.edu.au

Website: www.ists.qimr.edu.au

Other organisations

British Agency for Adoption and Fostering (BAAF)

Skyline House
200 Union Street
London SE1 0LX

Tel: 0207 593 2000
Fax: 0207 593 2001

e-mail: mail@baaf.org.uk

Website: www.baaf.org.uk

Contact-a-Family

170 Tottenham Court Road
London W1P 0HA

Tel: 020 7383 3555
Fax: 020 7383 0259

e-mail: info@cafamily.org.uk

Website: www.cafamily.org.uk

continued over

Useful Addresses

Council for Awards in Children's Care and Education (CACHE)

8 Chequer Street
St Albans
Hertfordshire AL1 3XZ

Tel: 01727 847 636
Fax: 01727 867 609

Website: www.cache.org.uk

Contact local Higher Education College for details of nursery nurse training courses

Home Start
(providing volunteer support at home for families with under-5s)

2 Salisbury Road
Leicester LE1 7QR

Tel: 0116 233 9955
Fax: 0116 233 0232

e-mail: info@home-start.org.uk

Website: www.home-start.org.uk

In Touch Trust

10 Norman Road
Sale
Cheshire M33 3DF

Tel: 0161 905 2440
Fax: 0161 718 5787

e-mail: worthington@netscapeonline.co.uk

Useful Addresses

National Association of Toy and Leisure Libraries (NATLL)
(also known as Play Matters)

68 Churchway
London NW1 1LT

Tel: 020 7387 9592
Fax: 020 7383 2714

e-mail: admin@natll.ukf.net

Website: www.charitynet.org/~NATLL

National Childbirth Trust (NCT)

Alexandra House
Oldham Terrace
Acton
London W3 6NH

Helpline: 0208 992 8637 (9.30am - 4.30pm)
Fax: 0208 992 5929

Website: www.nct-online.org

All the organisations listed here are registered charities.

References

1   DA Hay, C Gleeson, C Davies, B Lorden, D Mitchell and L Paton. What information should the multiple birth family receive before, during and after the birth? *Acta Genet Med Gemellol* 39:259-269, 1990

2   EM Bryan. Newborn twins. In: *Twins and Higher Multiple Births: a Guide to their Nature and Nurture*, London: Edward Arnold, Ch6 97-111, 1992

3   JW McArthur. Genetics of quintuplets. I. Diagnosis of the Dionne quintuplets as a monozygotic set. *J Hered* 29:401, 1938

4   NM Fisk and EM Bryan. Routine prenatal determination of chorionicity in multiple gestation: a plea to the obstetrician. *Br J Obstet Gynaecol* 100:975-977, 1993

5   P Gringras. Identical differences - monozygotic twins with different hair colour. *Lancet* 353:562, 1999

6   DA Hay and PJ O'Brien. Early influences on the school social adjustment of twins. *Acta Genet Med Gemellol* 36:239-248, 1987

7   BJ Botting, AJ Macfarlane and FV Price (eds). *Three Four and More*, London: HMSO, 1990

8   EM Taylor and JL Emery. Maternal stress, family and health care of twins. *Children and Society* 4:351-366, 2000

9   J Haigh and L Wilkinson. Care and management of twins. *Health Visitor* 62:43-45, 1989

10 K Thorpe, J Golding, I MacGillivray and R Greenwood. Comparison of prevalence of depression in mothers of twins and mothers of singletons. *BMJ* 302:875-878, 1991

11 BA Broadbent. Twin trauma. *Nursing Times* 28-30, 1985

12 ER Goshen-Gottstein. The mothering of twins, triplets and quadruplets. *Psychiatry* 43:189-204, 1980

13 AJ Costello. Deprivation and family structure with particular reference to twins. In: *The Child in the Family. Vulnerable Children*, edited by EJ Anthony, C Koupernik and C Chiland, New York: John Wiley, vol 4, 1978

14 L Saint, P Maggiore and PE Hartmann. Yield and nutrient content of milk in eight women breast-feeding twins and one woman breast-feeding triplets. *Br J Nutrition* 56:49-58, 1986

References

15 KK Gromada and AK Sangler. Breastfeeding twins and higher-order multiples. *J Obstet Gynecol Neonatal Nursing* 27:441-449, 1998

16 HL Addy. The breast-feeding of twins. *J Trop Pediatr Env Child Health* 21:231-239, 1975

17 Department of Health, 1991

18 E Tyson. *Breastfeeding and the mother.* Ciba Foundation Symposium 45, London: Elsevier, 1976

19 R Hattori and H Hattori. Breastfeeding twins: guidelines for success. *Birth* 26:37-42, 1999

20 KH Nyqvist and LM Lutes. Co-bedding twins: a developmentally supportive care strategy. *J Obstet Gynecol Neonatal Nursing* 27:450-456, 1998

21 K DellaPorta, D Aforismo and M Butler-O'Hara. Co-bedding of twins in the neonatal intensive care unit. *Pediatric Nursing* 24:529-531, 1998

22 AJ Macfarlane, FV Price, EM Bryan and BJ Botting. Early days. In: *Three Four and More,* edited by BJ Botting, AJ Macfarlane and FV Price, London: HMSO, Ch6 80-98, 1990

23 RS Wilson. Growth standards for twins from birth to four years. *Ann Hum Biol* 1:175-188, 1974

24 JM Buckler. Growth and development of twins. In: *Twin and Triplet Psychology,* edited by AC Sandbank, London: Routledge, Ch9 143-166, 1999

25 T Husen. *Psychological Twin Research.* Stockholm: Almquist and Wiksell, 1959

26 JMH Buckler and M Green. Birth weight and head circumference standards for English twins. *Arch Dis Child* 71:516-521, 1994

27 RS Wilson. Twin growth: initial deficit recovery and trends in concordance from birth to nine years. *Ann Hum Biol* 6:205-220, 1979

28 RS Wilson. Twins and mental development in the pre-school years. *Devel Psychol* 10:580-588, 1974

29 L Murray and PJ Cooper. Effects of postnatal depression on infant development. *Arch Dis Child* 17:99-101, 1997

30 EM Bryan. The preschool twin. In: *Twins and Higher Multiple Births: a Guide to their Nature and Nurture,* London: Edward Arnold, Ch10 p138, 1992

References

31 J Burn. Disturbance of morphological laterality in humans. In: *Biology, Asymmetry and Handedness*. Ciba Foundation Symposium, Chichester: John Wiley and Sons, 282-299, 1991

32 E Day. The development of language in twins. I. A comparison of twins and single children. *Child Dev* 3:179-199, 1932

33 EA Davis. *Linguistic Skill in Twins, Singletons and Siblings and Only Children from Age Five to Ten Years*, University of Minnesota: Instit Child Welfare, Monograph Series 14, 1937

34 I Alm. The longterm prognosis for prematurely born children. *Acta Padiatr* 42(Suppl 94):9-116, 1953

35 P Mittler. Language development in young twins: biological, genetic and social aspects. *Acta Genet Med Gemellol* 25:359-365, 1976

36 DA Hay, M Prior, S Collett and M Williams. Speech and language development in preschool twins. *Acta Genet Med Gemellol* 36:213-223, 1987

37 S McMahon and B Dodd. A comparison of the expressive communication skills of triplet, twin and singleton children. *Eur J Disorders Communication* 32:328-345, 1997

38 DA Hay, PJ O'Brien, CJ Johnston and M Prior. The high incidence of reading disability in twin boys and its implications for genetic analyses. *Acta Genet Med Gemellol* 33:223-236, 1984

39 F Levy, D Hay, M McLaughlin, C Wood and I Waldman. Twin sibling differences in parental reports of ADHD, speech, reading and behaviour problems. *J Child Psychol Psychiatry* 37:569-578, 1996

40 P Tymms and P Preedy. The attainment and progress of twins at the start of school. *Educational Research* 40:244-249, 1998

41 H Lytton. *Parent-Child Interaction. The Socialization Process Observed in Twin and Singleton Families*, New York: Plenum Press, 1980

42 P Mittler. Biological and social aspects of language development in twins. *Dev Med Child Neurol* 12:741-757, 1970

43 R Zazzo. The twin condition and the couple effects on personality development. *Acta Genet Med Gemellol* 25:343-352, 1979

44 HL Koch. *Twins and Twin Relations*, Chicago: University of Chicago Press, 1966

References

45 RS Wilson, AM Brown and AP Matheny. Emergence and persistence of behavioural differences in twins. *J Child Devel* 42:1381-1398, 1971

46 PS Very and NP Van Hine. Effects of birth order upon personality development of twins. *J Genet Psychol* 114:93-95, 1969

47 DL Vandell, MT Owen, KS Wilson and VK Henderson. Social development in infant twins: peer and mother child relationships. *Child Devel* 59:168-177, 1988

48 MH Klaus and JH Kennell. Mothers separated from their newborn infants. *Pediatr Clin North Am* 17:1015-1037, 1970

49 S Goldberg, M Perrotta, K Minde and C Corter. Maternal behavior and attachment in low-birth-weight twins and singletons. *Child Devel* 57:34-46,1986

50 JR Spillman. *The Role of Birthweight in Maternal-Twin Relationships*, Cranfield Institute of Technology, MSc Thesis, 1984

51 MG Allen, SI Greenspan and W Pollin. The effect of parental perceptions on early development in twins. *Psychiatry* 39:65-71, 1976

52 MG Allen. W Pollin and A Hoffer. Parental birth and infancy factors in infant twin development. *Am J Psychiatry* 127:1597-1604, 2000

53 ML Riese. Neonatal temperament in full-term pairs discordant for birth weight. *J Devel Behav Pediatrics* 15:342-347, 1994

54 K Minde, C Corter, S Goldberg and D Jeffers. Maternal preference between premature twins up to age four. *J Am Acad Child Adolescent Psychiatry* 29:367-374, 1990

55 DA Hay, R McIndoe and PJ O'Brien. The older sibling of twins. *Aus J Early Child* 13:25-28, 1987

56 P Preedy. Meeting the educational needs of pre-school and primary aged twins and higher multiples. In: *Twin and Triplet Psychology*, edited by AC Sandbank, London: Routledge, Ch6 70-99, 1999

57 B Broadbent. *Twins in the Primary School: Twenty Pairs of Twins Observed*. An unpublished study, 1995

58 C Gleeson, DA Hay, CJ Johnston and TM Theobald. Twins in school: an Australia-wide program. *Acta Genet Med Gemellol* 39:231-244, 1990

References

59 CJ Phillips and M Watkinson. Characteristics of the families and similarity of environment within twin pairs. In: *Twin Research* (Birmingham 1968-72); vol 2, Part 1, edited by CJ Phillips, Centre for Child Study University of Birmingham, pp 2-57, 1981

60 F Stanley and B Petterson. Cerebral palsy in multiple births: the changing epidemiological patterns. In: *Multiple Pregnancy*, edited by RH Ward and M Whittle. London: RCOG, Ch31 309-325, 1995

61 F Falkner and AP Matheny. The long-term development of twins: anthropometric factors and cognition. In: *Multiple Pregnancy. Epidemiology, Gestation and Perinatal Outcome*, edited by LG Keith, E Papiernik, DM Keith and B Luke, Carnforth: Parthenon, Ch46 613-624, 1995

62 DA Hay. Adolescent twins and secondary schooling. In: *Twin and Triplet Psychology*, edited by AC Sandbank, London: Routledge, Ch8 119-142, 1999

63 M Tanimura, I Matsui and N Kobayashi. Child abuse of one of a pair of twins in Japan. *Lancet* 336:1298-1299, 1990

64 JR Groothius, WA Altemeir, JP Robarge, S O'Connor, H Sandler, P Vietze, RE Lustig Gross, HW Clatworthy and JA Meeker. Increased child abuse in families with twins. *Pediatrics* 70:769-773, 1982

65 EM Bryan. The death of a twin. In: *Twin and Triplet Psychology*, edited by AC Sandbank, London: Routledge, Ch11 186-200, 1999

66 EM Bryan. Death of a Twin. In: *Twins and Higher Multiple Births: a Guide to their Nature and Nurture*, London: Edward Arnold, Ch14 171-182, 1992

67 B Botting, I Macdonald-Davis and A Macfarlane. Recent trends in the incidence of multiple births and their mortality. *Arch Dis Child* 62:941-950, 1987

68 E Lewis and EM Bryan. Management of perinatal loss of a twin. *BMJ* 297:1321-1323, 1988

69 J Woodward. *The Lone Twin. Understanding Twin Bereavement and Loss*, London: Free Association Books Ltd, 1998

70 RG Carpenter, A Gardner, E Pursall, PM McWeeny and JL Emery. Identification of some infants at immediate risk of dying unexpectedly and justifying intensive study. *Lancet*, ii:343-346, 1979

References

71 S Beal. Some epidemiological factors about sudden infant death syndrome (sids) in South Australia. In: *Sudden Infant Death Syndrome*, edited by JT Tildon, LM Roeder and A Steinschneider, New York: Academic Press, pp 15-28, 1983

72 JL Emery. Cot death. *Maternal and Child Health* 4:374-378, 1979

73 EM Bryan. The problem with twins. *New Law Journal*, 142: 1570-1571, 1992

74 N Segal. Twist of fate: twins reared apart. In:*Entwined Lives. Twins and What They Tell Us*, New York: Dutton, Ch7 116-151, 1999

75 M Mugford and J Henderson. Resource implications of multiple births. In: *Multiple Pregnancy*, edited by RH Ward and M Whittle, London: RCOG Press, Ch 33 334-348, 1995

76 B Alin Akerman. The psychology of triplets. In: *Twin and Triplet Psychology*, edited by AC Sandbank, London: Routledge, Ch7 100-118, 1999

77 M Garel, C Salobir and B Blondel. Psychological consequences of having triplets: a 4-year follow-up study. *Fertil Steril* 67:1162-1165, 1997

Further Reading

For professionals

Other titles in the MBF Guidelines series

Facts About Multiple Births (1997)

Multiple Pregnancy (1997)

Bereavement (1997)

Special Needs in Twins and More (1999)

Books

Three, Four and More: A Study of Triplets and Higher Order Births. Edited by BJ Botting, AJ Macfarlane and FV Price. London: HMSO, 1990

Twins and Higher Multiple Births: a Guide to their Nature and Nurture. EM Bryan. Sevenoaks: Edward Arnold, 1992

Multiple Pregnancy. Edited by RH Ward and M Whittle. London: RCOG, 1995

Multiple Pregnancy. Epidemiology, Gestation and Perinatal Outcome. Edited by LG Keith, E Papiernik, DM Keith and B Luke. Carnforth: Parthenon, 1995

When You're Expecting Twins, Triplets or Quads. B Luke and T Eberlein. New York: Harper Perennial, 1999

Twin and Triplet Psychology. Edited by AC Sandbank. London: Routledge, 1999

Entwined Lives: Twins and What They Tell Us. N Segal. New York: Dutton, 1999

Iatrogenic Multiple Pregnancy: Clinical Implications. Edited by I Blickstein and LG Keith. Carnforth: Parthenon, 2000

Exploring Twins: Towards a Social Analysis of Twinship. EA Stewart. London: Macmillan, 2000